Essential Maths

Book 8H

Answers

Elmwood Press

First published 2009 by
Elmwood Press
80 Attimore Road
Welwyn Garden City
Herts. AL8 6LP
Tel. 01707 333232

ISBN 9781 902 214 856

Printed in Great Britain by Face Communications
www.facecommunications.co.uk

Unit 1

Page 1 **Exercise 1M**

1. 5, 13 **2.** 2, 3, 5, 7, 11, 13, 17, 19, 23, 29 **3.** 23, 41, 59, 71 (+ others) **4.** (a) 1, 2, 3, 4, 6, 12

(b) 1, 2, 3, 5, 6, 10, 15, 30 (c) 1, 17 (d) 1, 2, 5, 10, 25, 50 **5.** 21, 28

6. (a) 1, 2, 3, 4, 6, 8, 12, 24 (b) 1, 2, 4, 5, 8, 10, 20, 40 (c) 1, 2, 4, 8 **7.** (a) 1, 2, 4, 7, 14, 28

(b) 1, 2, 3, 4, 6, 9, 12, 18, 36 (c) 1, 2, 4 (d) 4 **8.** (a) 6 (b) 7 **9.** (a) $1 \times 28, 2 \times 14, 4 \times 7$

(b) $1 \times 30, 2 \times 15, 3 \times 10, 5 \times 6$ **10.** (a) $10 + 14, 9 + 15, 11 + 13$ (b) $5 + 13, 7 + 11$

11. (a) false (b) true (c) false **12.** (clockwise from top) (a) 5, 4, 11 (b) 7, 9, 5 (c) 6, 8, 9

Page 3 **Exercise 1E**

1. (a) 3, 6, 9, 12 (b) 7, 14, 21, 28 (c) 10, 20, 30, 40 (d) 15, 30, 45, 60 **2.** 60

3. LCM = 24 **4.** 80 **5.** (a) true (b) false (c) false **6.** true **7.** 13, 31, 67

8. 41 **9.** 59, 61 **10.** (a) one (b) one **11.** 17, 71; 37, 73; 79, 97

12. 10, 15 are next triangle numbers **13.** (a) $1 + 1 + 9 + 36$

(b) $1 + 1 + 4 + 16 + 25$ (c) $27 + 16 + 4$

Page 5 **Exercise 2M**

1. $108 = 2^2 \times 3^3, 300 = 2^2 \times 3 \times 5^2$ **2.** (a) $2^3 \times 3$ (b) 3^4 (c) $2^2 \times 3 \times 7$ (d) $2^3 \times 5^2$

(e) $2 \times 3 \times 7^2$ (f) $2 \times 3^2 \times 5 \times 7$ (g) $2^3 \times 7^2$ (h) $2^3 \times 3^2 \times 5 \times 11$ **3.** 7 **4.** 15

5. 25 **6.** 6, 49 **7.** 10, 18, 21 **8.** $13 = 4 + 9, 17 = 1 + 16, 29 = 4 + 25, 37 = 1 + 36,$

$41 = 16 + 25, 53 = 4 + 49, 61 = 25 + 36, 73 = 9 + 64, 89 = 25 + 64, 97 = 16 + 81$

9. 14 **10.** (a) 0 (b) 2 (c) 1 (d) 0

Page 6 **Exercise 2E**

1. (a) 64 (b) 125 (c) 216 (d) 1000 **2.** 64 **3.** 3, 5, 4

4. 9, 1, 32, 7, 10 000, 121, 10 000, 0.01, $\frac{1}{4}$, 1 000 000 **5.** <, = , <, <, <, >

6. clockwise from top left: 44, 50, 11, 100 **7.** (a) false (e.g. 64) (b) false ($x = 0$) (c) true **8.** 61

9. 16807, 15625, 0.125, 19.4481 **10.** 3, 7, 5 **11.** (a) 2^5 (b) 3^7 (c) 5^5 (d) 4^{10}

12. (a) 6^3 (b) n^3 **13.** yes **14.** $n = 7, m = 4$ (b) $n = 25, m = 10$ **15.** $a = 5, b = 10$

Page 8 **Exercise 1M**

1. (a) 6 (b) 5 (c) 5 (d) 2 (e) 25 (f) 30 (g) 12 (h) 6

2. $\frac{4}{10}, \frac{6}{15}, \frac{8}{20}, \frac{10}{25}$ etc. **3.** (a) $\frac{1}{3}$ (b) $\frac{1}{4}$ (c) $\frac{2}{5}$ (d) $\frac{5}{8}$ (e) $\frac{4}{7}$ (f) $\frac{5}{12}$ (g) $\frac{1}{50}$ (h) $\frac{17}{20}$

(i) $\frac{3}{11}$ (j) $\frac{2}{5}$ **4.** (a) ROME (b) MOSCOW **5.** (a) $1\frac{2}{3}$ (b) $1\frac{2}{5}$ (c) $2\frac{2}{5}$ (d) $3\frac{2}{3}$

(e) $2\frac{6}{7}$ (f) $7\frac{3}{10}$ (g) $4\frac{1}{8}$ (h) $8\frac{1}{5}$ (i) $8\frac{1}{2}$ (j) $2\frac{1}{250}$ (k) $6\frac{1}{3}$ (l) $6\frac{5}{7}$ **6.** (a) $\frac{13}{4}$

(b) $\frac{5}{2}$ (c) $\frac{19}{4}$ (d) $\frac{11}{5}$ (e) $\frac{16}{3}$ (f) $\frac{22}{3}$ (g) $\frac{24}{7}$ (h) $\frac{23}{9}$ (i) $\frac{12}{11}$ (j) $\frac{303}{50}$

Page 9 **Exercise 1E**

1. $\frac{3}{5}$ **2.** $\frac{10}{11}$ **3.** $\frac{7}{8}$ **4.** $\frac{11}{15}$ **5.** $\frac{4}{7}$ **6.** $\frac{2}{9}$ **7.** $\frac{3}{7}$ **8.** $\frac{1}{2}$

9. (a) $\frac{5}{10}$ (b) $\frac{7}{8}$ (c) $\frac{3}{12}$ **10.** $\frac{5}{8}$ **11.** $\frac{7}{18}$ **12.** $\frac{15}{20}$ **13.** $\frac{7}{8}$ **14.** $\frac{11}{16}$

15. $\frac{1}{6}$ **16.** $\frac{1}{4}$ **17.** $\frac{3}{8}$ **18.** $\frac{7}{12}$ **19.** $\frac{9}{10}$ **20.** $\frac{11}{15}$ **21.** $\frac{19}{20}$ **22.** $\frac{1}{30}$

23. $\frac{1}{12}$ **24.** $\frac{11}{24}$ **25.** $\frac{7}{22}$ **26.** $\frac{1}{2}+\frac{1}{3}+\frac{1}{6}$ **27.** $\frac{1}{2}+\frac{1}{4}+\frac{1}{5}+\frac{1}{20}$ **28.** $\frac{9}{40}$ **29.** $1\frac{5}{8}\,\text{g}$ **30.** $\frac{19}{48}$

Page 11 **Exercise 2M**

1. (a) $\frac{1}{12}$ (b) $\frac{3}{25}$ (c) $\frac{3}{20}$ **2.** (a) $\frac{6}{25}$ (b) $\frac{3}{28}$ (c) $\frac{3}{20}$ (d) $\frac{1}{8}$ (e) $\frac{5}{16}$

(f) $\frac{5}{8}$ (g) $\frac{3}{14}$ (h) $\frac{3}{40}$ (i) $\frac{2}{15}$ (j) $\frac{3}{22}$ (k) $\frac{1}{3}$ (l) $\frac{1}{3}$

3. $A=\frac{1}{4}\,\text{m}^2$, $B=\frac{1}{2}\,\text{m}^2$, $C=\frac{1}{12}\,\text{m}^2$, $D=\frac{1}{6}\,\text{m}^2$ **4.** (a) 12   (b) 9   (c) 54   (d) 30   (e) 15 km

(f) 42 kg   (g) 45 m   (h) £96   **5.** 45   **6.** (a) 3   (b) 3   (c) 5   (d) 7   (e) 20   (f) 60

Page 12 **Exercise 2E**

1. (a) $2\frac{1}{3}$ (b) 1   **2.** (a) $\frac{5}{8}$ (b) $\frac{5}{12}$ (c) $1\frac{1}{20}$ (d) 1   (e) $\frac{13}{40}$ (f) $2\frac{11}{20}$ (g) $3\frac{3}{4}$

(h) $12\frac{1}{4}$ **3.** $8\frac{1}{8}$ square inches   **4.** $4\frac{1}{2}$ **5.** (a) $10\frac{1}{2}$ (b) $6\frac{1}{4}$ (c) $9\frac{1}{3}$ (d) $7\frac{1}{2}$

(e) $\frac{2}{3}$ (f) $2\frac{1}{3}$ (g) $2\frac{3}{4}$ (h) $2\frac{2}{3}$ **6.** 32   **7.** (a) 4   (b) 9   (c) $\frac{6}{5}$ **8.** $\frac{11}{18},\frac{5}{8},\frac{23}{36},\frac{2}{3}$

9. (a) $\frac{1}{6}$ (b) $\frac{2}{3}$ (c) $\frac{2}{3}$ (d) $\frac{5}{6}$ (e) $\frac{9}{16}$ (f) $\frac{1}{3}+\frac{2}{5}$ (+ others)   **10.** (a) $\frac{3}{16}$ (b) $\frac{3}{8}$

(c) $\frac{1}{8}$ **11.**

+	$\frac{1}{4}$	$\frac{1}{6}$	$\frac{1}{2}$	$\frac{2}{3}$
$\frac{1}{3}$	$\frac{7}{12}$	$\frac{1}{2}$	$\frac{5}{6}$	1
$\frac{3}{8}$	$\frac{5}{8}$	$\frac{13}{24}$	$\frac{7}{8}$	$1\frac{1}{24}$
$\frac{1}{5}$	$\frac{9}{20}$	$\frac{11}{30}$	$\frac{7}{10}$	$\frac{13}{15}$
$\frac{1}{2}$	$\frac{3}{4}$	$\frac{2}{3}$	1	$1\frac{1}{6}$

12. $2\frac{5}{12}$ **13.** (a) $3\frac{13}{20}$ (b) $3\frac{5}{12}$ (c) $4\frac{1}{6}$ (d) $\frac{2}{3}$

(e) $1\frac{7}{12}$ (f) $6\frac{1}{10}$

14. 200   **15.** (a)

$\frac{1}{10}$	$\frac{9}{20}$	$\frac{1}{5}$
$\frac{7}{20}$	$\frac{1}{4}$	$\frac{3}{20}$
$\frac{3}{10}$	$\frac{1}{20}$	$\frac{2}{5}$

(b)

$\frac{5}{24}$	$\frac{1}{6}$	$\frac{3}{8}$
$\frac{5}{12}$	$\frac{1}{4}$	$\frac{1}{12}$
$\frac{1}{8}$	$\frac{1}{3}$	$\frac{7}{24}$

Page 15 **Exercise 3M**

1. (a) 3   (b) 6   (c) 12   **2.** (a) 4   (b) 12   (c) 24   **3.** (a) 20

(b) 15   (c) 14   **4.** (a) 5   (b) 6   (c) 10   (d) 4   (e) 27   (f) 36

5. (b) Right hand column: 60, 30, 20, 15, 12   **6.** (a) 20   (b) 24   (c) 20   (d) 6   (e) 22   (f) 25

Page 16 **Exercise 3E**

1. 2 **2.** $\frac{2}{3}$ **3.** $2\frac{1}{4}$ **4.** $1\frac{1}{3}$ **5.** $\frac{2}{5}$ **6.** $2\frac{1}{2}$ **7.** $\frac{15}{16}$ **8.** 3 **9.** $2\frac{1}{2}$ **10.** $\frac{3}{5}$

11. $\frac{50}{63}$ **12.** $3\frac{1}{2}$ **13.** $\frac{5}{7}$ **14.** $\frac{3}{4}$ **15.** $7\frac{1}{3}$ **16.** $\frac{1}{6}$ **17.** $\frac{1}{5}$ **18.** $\frac{5}{42}$ **19.** $\frac{2}{27}$ **20.** $\frac{5}{33}$

21. 14 **22.** 24 **23.** 8 **24.** 50 **25.** 36 mm

Page 17 **Exercise 1M**

1. 35 cm² **2.** 40 cm² **3.** 12 cm² **4.** 27 cm² **5.** 33 cm² **6.** 20 cm² **7.** (a) m² (b) km²
(c) mm² or cm² **8.** (a) 40 cm (b) 40 cm **9.** $1 \times 24, 2 \times 12, 3 \times 8$ **10.** 36
11. (a) D (b) B (c) C and D

Page 19 **Exercise 1E**

1. 40 cm² **2.** 42 cm² **3.** 40 cm² **4.** 70 cm² **5.** 25 cm² **6.** 24 cm² **7.** 24 cm²
8. 6 cm **9.** 2, 15; 3, 10; 5, 6 etc **10.** (a) 10 000 (b) 1000 000

Page 20 **Exercise 2M**

1. £178.50 **2.** 40 hectares **3.** 800 m **4.** A 64 cm², B 48 cm²
5. £6 **7.** $10 \rightarrow 15$ cm² **8.** 42 m² **9.** 9 cm **10.** 100 cm

Page 21 **Exercise 2E**

1. 8 cm **2.** 17 cm **3.** 9 cm **4.** 14.1 cm **5.** 7.9 cm **6.** 1.7 cm **7.** (a) 7 cm × 12 cm
(b) 6.5 cm × 10 cm **8.** 65 cm² **9.** (a) 12 (b) 10.5 (c) 14.5 (d) 11.5

Page 23 **Find the connection**

The areas of triangles 1, 2 and 3 are each equal to the area of the shaded triangle. This is known as Cross'
Theorem. (The result was found by a schoolboy called David Cross).

Page 23 **Check Yourself Sections 1.1, 1.2 and 1.3**

1.1 (a) 2, 3, 5, 7, 11, 13, 17, 19, 23 (b) $2 + 3 = 5$ (many others) (c) 28 (others)
(d) 1, 2, 3, 4, 5, 6, 8, 10, 12, 15, 20, 24, 30, 40, 60, 120 (e) 7, 14, 21, 28, 35 (f) (i) $9 + 36$
(ii) $25 + 81$ (iii) $9 + 64$ (g) (i) 9 (ii) 32 (iii) 10 000 (iv) 1000 000
1.2 (a) (i) $\frac{13}{14}$ (ii) $\frac{7}{24}$ (iii) $1\frac{1}{12}$ (b) (i) $1\frac{2}{45}$ (ii) $3\frac{1}{3}$ (iii) $\frac{1}{4}$
1.3 (a) (i) 54 cm², 36 cm (ii) 21 cm², 21.5 cm (b) base 5 cm, ht. 12 cm (c) 900 m

Page 25 **Exercise 1M**

1. (a) −1 (b) 2 (c) 3 (d) −3 (e) −4 (f) 3 (g) −5 (h) −1 (i) −6 (j) −1
(k) −3 (l) 5 **2.** (a) −5 (b) −6 (c) −1 (d) 0 (e) −4 (f) −2 (g) −8
(h) −10 (i) −20 (j) −16 (k) 3 (l) 14 **3.** (a) 0, −3 (b) −5 (c) −20, −15

4. (a)

+	7	–1	4	–2
1	8	0	5	–1
–3	4	–4	1	–5
2	9	1	6	0
5	12	4	9	3

(b)

+	–5	3	8	1
–1	–6	2	7	0
2	–3	5	10	3
4	–1	7	12	5
–2	–7	1	6	–1

Page 26   *Exercise 1E*

1. (a) 3   (b) –1   (c) 0   (d) –4   (e) 6   (f) –1   (g) 4   (h) 6   (i) 9   (j) 8
(k) 8   (l) 5   **2.** (a) 6   (b) 12   (c) –2   (d) 1   (e) 10   (f) 3   (g) 11   (h) 6
(i) –10   (j) –1   (k) –3   (l) 1   **3.** 52°C   **4.** (a) 2   (b) –4.5   (c) –11.5

5. (a)

0	5	–2
–1	1	3
4	–3	2

(b)

4	–3	2
–1	1	3
0	5	–2

(c)

–2	3	–4
–3	–1	1
2	–5	0

(d)

8	–1	2	–3
3	–4	9	–2
1	6	–5	4
–6	5	0	7

(e)

–7	4	–1	6
0	5	–6	3
2	–5	8	–3
7	–2	1	–4

6. (a) 15   (b) –11   **7.**

a	9	3	8	3	2	5	4	7	1	1
b	5	5	3	7	–2	–2	6	10	4	2
a – b	4	–2	5	–4	4	7	–2	–3	–3	–1

a	–3	4	3	5	7	4	6	7	2	0
b	0	9	–3	–1	–1	–6	0	5	–1	2
a – b	–3	–5	6	6	8	10	6	2	3	–2

8. (a)

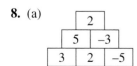

(b)

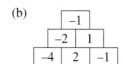

(c)

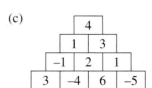

(d)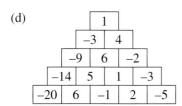

(e)
```
              -3
           -1    -2
         -3    2    -4
       -7   4   -2   -2
     -8   1   3   -5   3
```

(f)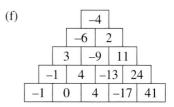

Page 29   Exercise 2M

1. −10   **2.** −8   **3.** −14   **4.** 6   **5.** 3   **6.** 4   **7.** −10   **8.** −5   **9.** −8   **10.** 9

11. −18   **12.** 8   **13.** −6   **14.** 8   **15.** −3   **16.** 5   **17.** 20   **18.** −4   **19.** 3   **20.** −3

21. (a) 14   (b) −18   (c) −1   (d) −30   (e) 4   (f) −4   (g) 20   (h) −23   (i) −8

    (j) 0   (k) 9   (l) −18   **22.** (a) −3   (b) −4   (c) 2   (d) −1   (e) −3   (f) −2

    (g) −6   (h) −20   (i) −10   (j) −2   (k) −2   (l) 1

23.

3	−1	−3	3

24.

−5	3	−15	−45

25.

−1	−2	2	−4

26.

3	−2	−6	12	−72

27.

−2	−1	2	−2	−4

28.

2	−3	−6	18	−108

29.

3	−1	−3	3	−9

30.

−1	4	−4	−16	64

31.

−5	2	−10	−20	200

Page 30   Exercise 2E

1. (a) 6   (b) − 1   (c) − 28   (d) 1   (e) − 9   (f) 0   (g) − 13   (h) − 48   (i) − 9

    (j) 4   (k) 10   (l) − 1   **2.** (a) − 10   (b) − 2   (c) 15   (d) − 2   (e) 13   (f) 3

    (g) − 14   (h) − 2   (i) 10   (j) 0   (k) 16   (l) − 1   **3.** (a) − 5   (b) − 1   (c) − 2

    (d) 1   (e) − 1   (f) − 5   (g) 6   (h) − 27   (i) − 0.5   (j) 36   (k) − 12   (l) 1

4. maximum 9°C, minimum − 5°C

5. Add

Add	−2	4	−5	3	−1
−3	−5	1	−8	0	−4
0	−2	4	−5	3	−1
1	−1	5	−4	4	0
5	3	9	0	8	4
−2	−4	2	−7	1	−3

6.

×	−2	5	3	−1	4
−4	8	−20	−12	4	16
6	−12	30	18	−6	24
−3	6	−15	−9	3	−12
−1	2	−5	−3	1	−4
5	−10	25	15	−5	20

7. (a) −2, 5   (b) −4, 3   (c) −2, 6   **8.** (a) −2, −5   (b) −3, −10   (c) −2, −3

    (d) −1, 6   (e) −2, −6   (f) −5, 3   (g) −6, −7

Page 31   **Practice tests**

Test 1

1. – 16   **2.** 64   **3.** – 15   **4.** – 2   **5.** 15   **6.** 18   **7.** 3   **8.** – 6   **9.** 11   **10.** – 48
11. – 7   **12.** 9   **13.** 6   **14.** – 18   **15.** – 10   **16.** 8   **17.** – 6   **18.** – 30   **19.** 4   **20.** – 1

Test 2

1. 100   **2.** – 20   **3.** – 8   **4.** – 7   **5.** – 4   **6.** 10   **7.** 9   **8.** – 10   **9.** 7   **10.** 35
11. – 20   **12.** – 24   **13.** – 10   **14.** – 7   **15.** – 19   **16.** – 1   **17.** – 5   **18.** – 13   **19.** 0   **20.** 8

Test 3

1. – 16   **2.** 6   **3.** – 13   **4.** 42   **5.** – 4   **6.** – 4   **7.** – 12   **8.** – 20   **9.** 6   **10.** 0
11. 36   **12.** – 10   **13.** – 7   **14.** 10   **15.** 6   **16.** – 18   **17.** – 9   **18.** 15   **19.** 1   **20.** 0

Test 4

1. 0   **2.** – 16   **3.** – 14   **4.** 24   **5.** – 1   **6.** 14   **7.** – 2   **8.** – 2   **9.** 7   **10.** 33
11. – 1   **12.** – 30   **13.** – 28   **14.** 19   **15.** – 9   **16.** – 8   **17.** 1   **18.** – 9   **19.** – 16   **20.** 4

Page 33   **Exercise 1M**

1. 5   **2.** 0   **3.** 14   **4.** 16   **5.** 15   **6.** 1.4   **7.** 1   **8.** 19   **9.** 4000   **10.** – 5   **11.** 70
12. 0.01   **13.** 81   **14.** 97   **15.** 7   **16.** (a) 162   (b) 7   (c) 1   (d) 5, 8, 11, 14, 17, 20
17. 720   **18.** 720   **19.** $\frac{5}{15}$ **20.** $\frac{5}{13}$ **21.** $5n$ **22.** 1   **23.** 2.13   **24.** 4.0   **25.** 1.0   **26.** 0.4
27. (a) $10^2 = 1 + 3 + 5 + ... + 17 + 19$ (b) $n = 199$

Page 34   **Exercise 1E**

1. 7, 18, 29, 40, 51   **2.** (a) add 2   (b) subtract 5   (c) multiply by 2   (d) divide by 3   **3.** (a) + 0.2
(b) ÷ 2   (c) – 0.15   (d) × 10   (d) ÷ 2   (f) – 3   **4.** (a) 17, 21, 25, 29, 33   (b) 5, 3, 1, – 1, – 3
(c) 5, 10, 20, 40, 80   (d) 8000, 800, 80, 8, 0.8   **5.** (a) 61   (b) 4, 79   (c) 3, 15, 31
(d) 5, 11, 23   **6.** (a) 14   (b) 3, 68   (c) 11, 32, 95   **7.** (a) × 3, + 1   (b) × 2, – 2
(c) × 3, – 2   **8.** (a) 7, 22, 27   (b) 30, 24, 18   (c) 47, 35, 29, 23   **9.** (a) 28   (b) 43
(c) 8   (d) 19   **10.** (a) $5 \times 99 = 495, 6 \times 99 = 594$ b) $9 \times 99 = 891$
11. 1111088889, 1111111088888889   **12.** many possibilities   **13.** (a) 5, 3.5, 2, 0.5, –1, –2.5
(b) 31104, 5184, 864, 144, 24, 4   (c) –7, –4, –1, 2, 5, 8   (d) 700, 70, 7, 0.7, 0.07, 0.007
(e) 2, 3, 5, 8, 13, 21   (f) 0, 2, 2, 4, 6, 10   (g) 1, 3, 3, 9, 27, 243   (h) 4, 9, 16, 25, 36, 49

Page 37   **Exercise 2M**

1. 13, 18   **2.** (a) 21, 27   (b) 37, 46   (c) 30, 38   **3.** (a) 24, 30   (b) 56, 73   (c) 55, 71   **4.** 60

Page 39   **Exercise 2E**

1. (a) Diagram 4 has 63 squares   (b) Diagram 5 has 99 squares   **2.** Diagram 6 requires 81 sticks
3. (a) 46, 61   (b) 58, 81   (c) 76, 104   **4.** (a) 145   (b) Row B 127, Row C 109
5. (b) 42, 16, 5   **6.** (a) 135   (b) 223   (c) 136   **7.** (a) 26   (b) 13 storeys

Page 42   Check Yourself Sections 1.4 and 1.5

1. (a) (i) -10 (ii) -14 (iii) -13 (iv) 50   (b)

1	6	−1
0	2	4
5	−2	3

  (v) 81   (vi) -0.8 (vii) -7 (viii) -40

2. (a) (i) 30   (ii) 48   (iii) 6   (b) (i) -3 (ii) -28 (iii) 11   **3.** (a) (i) 53   (ii) 1

  (iii) 0.034   (b) (i) 2, 10, 18, 26, 34   (ii) 240, 120, 60, 30, 15, 7.5   (c) (i) 31, 39   (ii) 49, 71

Page 43   Exercise 1M [some questions have more than one correct answer].

1. 19   **2.** 3   **3.** 36   **4.** 34   **5.** 10   **6.** 58   **7.** 26   **8.** 51   **9.** 3   **10.** 33   **11.** 52   **12.** 1

13. $9 + 3 \times 3 = 18$ **14.** $7 \times 3 + 11 = 32$ **15.** $6 + 12 \div 3 = 10$ **16.** $11 - 4 \div 4 = 10$

17. $15 + 4 \times 5 = 35$ **18.** $8 \times 3 + 6 = 30$ **19.** $7 + 6 \div 2 = 10$ **20.** $9 - 10 \div 5 = 7$

21. $6 \div 3 + 2 + 4 = 8$ **22.** $10 - 8 \div 2 = 6$ **23.** $8 \div 4 + 4 \times 4 = 18$ **24.** $9 - 2 \times 2 + 5 = 10$

25. $(7 - 2) \times 3 = 15$ **26.** $4 \times (2 + 5) = 28$ **27.** $(9 - 3) \times 6 = 36$ **28.** $(8 + 7) \div 3 = 5$

29. $20 \div (8 + 2) = 2$ **30.** $(7 - 2) \times (5 + 1) = 30$ **31.** $(3 + 11) \times 3 = 42$ **32.** $15 \div (8 - 9 \div 3) = 3$

33. $(8 - 4) \div (10 - 6) = 1$ **34.** $(3 \times 2 + 4) \times 2 = 20$ **35.** $18 - (1 + 2 + 3) = 12$ **36.** $4 \times (8 - 6 \div 2) = 20$

Page 44   Exercise 1E

1. 4.18   **2.** 14.66   **3.** 0.12   **4.** 1.55   **5.** 7.44   **6.** 29.21   **7.** 0.37   **8.** 3.19

9. 13.18   **10.** 1.20   **11.** 11.81   **12.** 1.32   **13.** 7.73   **14.** 10.57   **15.** 8.35   **16.** 6.74

17. 16.88   **18.** 10.16   **19.** 9.84   **20.** 4.87   **21.** 8.4   **22.** 12.31   **23.** 7.32   **24.** 2.16

25. 0.63   **26.** 12.17   **27.** 110   **28.** 10.21   **29.** 2.53   **30.** 2.91

Page 45   Exercise 2M

1. 3.36   **2.** 13.13   **3.** 4.99   **4.** 10.39   **5.** 0.92   **6.** 2.96   **7.** 1.99   **8.** 2.04

9. 0.90   **10.** 9.93   **11.** 6.87   **12.** 20.94   **13.** 3.89   **14.** 7.05   **15.** 11.95   **16.** 7.12

17. 3.69   **18.** 1.31   **19.** 5.73   **20.** 2.77   **21.** 23.41   **22.** 16.89   **23.** 1.61   **24.** 0.13

25. 7.08   **26.** 0.80   **27.** 14.08   **28.** 1.23   **29.** 9.10   **30.** 2.04

Page 46   Exercise 3M

1. $\frac{11}{12}$ **2.** $1\frac{1}{6}$ **3.** $1\frac{2}{9}$ **4.** $\frac{23}{30}$ **5.** $\frac{1}{10}$ **6.** $\frac{13}{16}$ **7.** $\frac{3}{14}$ **8.** $\frac{19}{30}$ **9.** $\frac{19}{20}$ **10.** $\frac{1}{6}$ **11.** $\frac{2}{9}$

12. $\frac{3}{44}$ **13.** $2\frac{11}{12}$ **14.** $2\frac{1}{6}$ **15.** $5\frac{1}{8}$ **16.** $3\frac{11}{12}$ **17.** $4\frac{4}{5}$ **18.** 6   **19.** $8\frac{3}{4}$ **20.** 4   **21.** (a) $3\frac{9}{20}$

  (b) $1\frac{1}{6}$ (c) $\frac{11}{12}$ (d) $1\frac{5}{28}$ (e) $1\frac{1}{3}$ (f) $\frac{5}{14}$

Page 46   Exercise 3E

1. $\frac{29}{80}$ **2.** $\frac{13}{24}$ **3.** $\frac{9}{100}$ **4.** $2\frac{7}{8}$ **5.** $\frac{3}{4}$ **6.** $1\frac{3}{8}$

7.

+	$\frac{1}{8}$	$\frac{3}{5}$	$\frac{1}{3}$	$1\frac{3}{4}$
$\frac{1}{2}$	$\frac{5}{8}$	$1\frac{1}{10}$	$\frac{5}{6}$	$2\frac{1}{4}$
$\frac{1}{4}$	$\frac{3}{8}$	$\frac{17}{20}$	$\frac{7}{12}$	2
$2\frac{1}{2}$	$2\frac{5}{8}$	$3\frac{1}{10}$	$2\frac{5}{6}$	$4\frac{1}{4}$
$\frac{2}{5}$	$\frac{21}{40}$	1	$\frac{11}{15}$	$2\frac{3}{20}$

×	$\frac{1}{2}$	$\frac{2}{3}$	$\frac{5}{8}$	$2\frac{1}{5}$
$\frac{4}{5}$	$\frac{2}{5}$	$\frac{8}{15}$	$\frac{1}{2}$	$1\frac{19}{25}$
$\frac{1}{3}$	$\frac{1}{6}$	$\frac{2}{9}$	$\frac{5}{24}$	$2\frac{8}{15}$
$\frac{1}{4}$	$\frac{1}{8}$	$\frac{1}{6}$	$\frac{5}{32}$	$2\frac{9}{20}$
$1\frac{1}{2}$	$\frac{3}{4}$	1	$\frac{15}{16}$	$3\frac{7}{10}$

8. $2\frac{2}{9}$ **9.** $\frac{1}{14}$ **10.** $\frac{16}{27}$ **11.** $\frac{4}{15}$ **12.** $25\frac{1}{2}$ **13.** $-\frac{7}{30}$ **14.** $\frac{3}{5}$ **15.** $\frac{4}{7}$ **16.** $2\frac{1}{2}$

Page 47   **Exercise 4M**

1. −21   **2.** 10   **3.** −2   **4.** −40   **5.** 4   **6.** −4   **7.** 8.5   **8.** −3.4   **9.** 15
10. 1.21   **11.** 32   **12.** −68   **13.** 6   **14.** −2   **15.** −2   **16.** −9.69   **17.** −1.4   **18.** 8.34
19. −2.64   **20.** 60.04   **21.** 20.25   **22.** −263.5   **23.** 6.4   **24.** (a) −28   (b) −3.3   (c) −7.01

Page 48   **Exercise 5M**

1. 23.8   **2.** 12.2   **3.** 24.6   **4.** 123   **5.** 44.7   **6.** 14.8   **7.** £18.02   **8.** £13.30   **9.** £72.08   **10.** £35.80

Page 49   **Exercise 5E**

1. 50.7   **2.** 19.4   **3.** 398.3   **4.** 11.9   **5.** 323.2   **6.** 27.3   **7.** 18.7   **8.** 12.6   **9.** 46.2
10. 1.2   **11.** 1.0   **12.** 4.4   **13.** 9.9   **14.** 2.3   **15.** 1.2   **16.** 99.1   **17.** 1.0   **18.** 0.5
19. 1.6   **20.** 29.7   **21.** 37.7   **22.** 18.8   **23.** 171.2   **24.** 165.0   **25.** 2.8   **26.** 4.3   **27.** 1.8

Page 50   **Crossword Puzzle**

¹L	I	²E	S		³H	⁴I
I		E		⁵L	E	G
⁶O	I	L	⁷B	E	L	L
S			⁸O	S	L	O
	⁹B	¹⁰O	O	H	O	O
		¹¹O	Z	L		
¹²S	H	O	E		¹³H	E

Page 51   **Check Yourself Section 1.6**

1. **1.** 18   **2.** 70   **3.** 9   **4.** 80   **5.** 5   **6.** 44   **2.** (a) 0.8   (b) 43.1   (c) $2\frac{17}{30}$
(d) 10.8   (e) 4.1   (f) 1.9   (g) 1.2   (h) 252.6

Page 51 *Unit 1 Mixed Review*

Part one

1. 11, 19, 37 **2.** (a) 1, 3, 5, 15 (b) 1, 2, 3, 4, 6, 8, 12, 24 (c) 1, 2, 3, 5, 6, 10, 15, 30

3. (a) 2000 (b) 48 (c) 40 (d) 2.9 (e) 0.5 (f) 35

4. (a) 29 (b) 7, 17 (c) 3, 9, 21 **5.** (a) add $\frac{1}{2}$ (b) double (c) subtract 0.2

6. (a) 33 (b) 72 (c) 229 **7.** 35 hours 15 minutes **8.** (a) -5

(b) -3 (c) -8 (d) 6 (e) 6 (f) -12 (g) 0 (h) -18

9. (a)

6	7	2
1	5	9
8	3	4

(b)

-4	3	-5
-3	-2	-1
1	-7	0

10. (a) 5 (b) 20 (c) 8 (d) 9 **11.** (a) 12 cm² (b) 40 cm² (c) 20 cm² **12.** 32 cm²

13. (a) $\frac{3}{8}$ (b) $\frac{7}{8}$ (c) $\frac{3}{10}$ (d) $\frac{1}{2}$ (e) 40 (f) 24 (g) 200 (h) $\frac{11}{12}$ **14.** (a) 22

(b) 41 (c) 25 (d) 32 (e) 11 (f) 16 **15.** (a) 13.3 (b) 3.3 (c) $3\frac{9}{10}$

(d) 7.2 (e) 1.5 (f) 3

Part two

1. 31 cm² **2.** (a) 16 (b) 8 (c) 1 (d) 875 **3.** (a) 3.9 (b) 2.6 (c) 11.6 (d) 2.9 **4.** 1260

5. (a) 22 (b) 51 **6.** left to right: 48, 32, 45, 300 **7.** $2^2 \times 3^4 = 324$ **8.** 5.5 square units

9.

1 2	4	2 2		3 6
5		4 1	5 3	5
6 1	7 9		2	
	8 8	1		9 5
10 9		11 6	2	4

10. $\frac{1}{6}$ **11.** 14 cm **12.** 120 m **13.** (a) $\frac{5}{9}$ (b) $1\frac{1}{2}$ (c) $\frac{2}{21}$

(d) $5\frac{1}{4}$ (e) $3\frac{1}{8}$ (f) $\frac{21}{44}$ **14.** 88 cm

Puzzles and Problems 1

Cross numbers

A

¹3•	4	5		²2	9		³7
3		⁴8	0	3		⁵1	9
⁶7	0	7		⁷5	⁸1	2	6
5		⁹5	¹⁰9	9	1	7	
	¹¹2		7		9•		¹²1
¹³3	9	¹⁴9		¹⁵3	9	•¹⁶2	5
1		¹⁷9	6	9		7	7
¹⁸5	0	0	0		¹⁹1	2	•5

B

¹1	2	3		²1	3		³3
5		⁴1	9	2		⁵4	9
⁶9	3	4		⁷8	•⁸1	1	8
9		⁹8	¹⁰1	3	0	1•	
	¹¹7		2		0		¹²8
¹³2	8	¹⁴8		¹⁵9	1	¹⁶3	7
9•		¹⁷5	7	0		3	8
¹⁸6	4	8	2		¹⁹1	9	•4

C

¹2	2	5		²3	6		³1
7		⁴6	2	5		⁵9	0•
⁶7	0	2		⁷5	⁸1	•1	9
5•		⁹1	¹⁰9	4	3	9	
	¹¹4		9		2		¹²2
¹³1	0	¹⁴6		¹⁵6	0	¹⁶1	7
0		¹⁷3	•0	5		9	4
¹⁸5	1	•4	0		¹⁹1	2	9

Page 58   **Mental Arithmetic Practice**

1. 110   2. 1 million   3. 120 cm   4. £8.50   5. 20   6. £5

7. 15 miles   8. 11.5   9. 32   10. 60°   11. 300 cm²   12. 229 (in 2009)

13. $\frac{2}{5}$ 14. 8   15. 50, 20, 2, 2, 1 or 20, 20, 20, 10, 5 or 50, 10, 5, 5, 5

16. 380 m   17. 30   18. £707   19. false   20. 2 pounds (2.2)

21. £1.50   22. 12   23. £200   24. 144   25. true

26. £1.88   27. 100°   28. 12   29. 90°   30. 37

Page 59   **A long time ago!**

1. (a) $\frac{3}{8}$ (b) $\frac{3}{32}$ (c) $\frac{17}{64}$ (d) $\frac{13}{16}$ (e) $\frac{3}{64}$ (f) $\frac{29}{32}$

2. Possibly   (a)   (b)

(c)    (d)

3. (a) $\frac{63}{64}$ (b) $\frac{1}{64}$

Unit 2

Page 61   *Exercise 1M*

1. 1455	**2.** 6324	**3.** 1416	**4.** 5250	**5.** 1302	**6.** 8.37	**7.** 1712	**8.** 2205
9. 60000	**10.** 0.653	**11.** 17000	**12.** 56.2	**13.** 2920	**14.** 1.37	**15.** 0.83	**16.** 0.219
17. 4830	**18.** 7800	**19.** 24800	**20.** 7971	**21.** 0.0462	**22.** 867	**23.** 1580	**24.** 2800
25. 13.4	**26.** 7.8	**27.** 1384	**28.** 124	**29.** 14.1	**30.** 0.128	**31.** 0.732	**32.** 510

Page 62   *Exercise 1E*

1. 1.7	**2.** £5.75	**3.** £8.65	**4.** 66	**5.** 48.02	**6.** 1.37	**7.** 1327	**8.** 8.55
9. 2415	**10.** 3736	**11.** 2.62	**12.** 2.13	**13.** 20800	**14.** 257.4	**15.** 0.102	**16.** 10400
17. 0.0231	**18.** 0.655	**19.** 2190	**20.** 0.057	**21.** (a) 0.4	(b) 0.25		

22. (a) 100   (b) 6.23   (c) 1.15   (d) 200   (e) 0.0067   (f) 5.38

Page 63   *Exercise 2M*

1. 6.5, 9.5   **2.** 0.5, 3.5   **3.** 15, 45   **4.** 0.62, 0.66   **5.** 0.65, 0.8   **6.** 10.5, 12

7. 46, 56   **8.** 0.212, 0.218   **9.** 2.3, 2.8   **10.** 0.5, 1.2, 1.25, 1.5   **11.** 1, 3.5, 412.5, 480

12. 250, 440, 0.9, 2.5   **13.** 0.44, 0.6   **14.** 0.12, 0.34   **15.** 180, 320   **16.** 0.7, 1.8

17. 0.266, 0.276   **18.** 0.89, 1.04   **19.** 6.8, 8.5   **20.** 1200, 2500

Page 64   *Exercise 2E*

1. (a) 0.7, 0.718, 0.73   (b) 0.405, 0.41, 0.5   (c) 0.029, 0.035, 0.3   (d) 0.0511, 0.058, 0.06

2. (a) 0.5   (b) 0.45   (c) 0.05   (d) 0.15   (e) 0.065

3. (a) >   (b) <   (c) =   (d) >   (e) >   (f) <

4. (a) 3.3   (b) 0.629   (c) 6.39   (d) 0.425   **5.** (a) 2.7, 2.71   (b) 1.49, 1.48

    (c) 4.2   (d) 4.99, …, 5.03   **6.** (a) +0.02   (b) −0.002   (c) +0.01   (d) +0.001

7. (a) 180 mm, 30 cm, 0.00035 km, 0.002 km, 4.1 m   (b) 585 mm, 0.62 m, 118 cm, 0.008 km, 50 000 mm

Page 65   *Exercise 3M*

1. 0.8	**2.** 0.3	**3.** 1.2	**4.** 2.6	**5.** 0.04	**6.** 0.07	**7.** 0.09	**8.** 0.024
9. 0.08	**10.** 0.06	**11.** 0.15	**12.** 0.07	**13.** 0.52	**14.** 0.63	**15.** 0.006	**16.** 0.052
17. 1.1	**18.** 0.9	**19.** 0.23	**20.** 0.05	**21.** (a) ×100, ÷1000, ×10, ÷100			

    (b) ÷10, ÷10, ×100, ÷100   (c) ×100, ÷10, ÷100, ÷10   (d) ÷100, ÷10, ×10000, ÷100

Page 66   *Exercise 3E*

1. 1.4	**2.** 2.4	**3.** 2.4	**4.** 0.15	**5.** 2.1	**6.** 0.46	**7.** 0.45	**8.** 0.36
9. 0.6	**10.** 0.49	**11.** 0.8	**12.** 4.2	**13.** 0.45	**14.** 0.016	**15.** 0.0006	**16.** 0.66
17. 0.36	**18.** 0.64	**19.** 0.56	**20.** 1.05	**21.** 1.083	**22.** 1.26	**23.** 0.217	**24.** 0.0084
25. 0.0066	**26.** 0.324	**27.** 0.5677	**28.** 12.96	**29.** 0.253	**30.** 9.27	**31.** 0.04	**32.** 0.16

33. (a) €50   (b) $78   (c) $1560   **34.** (a) 1.8   (b) 6   (c) 0.3   (d) 100   (e) 2.2   (f) 0.03

Page 67   ***Exercise 4M***

1. 13.02   **2.** 169.6   **3.** 70.5   **4.** 64.6   **5.** 171   **6.** 449.4   **7.** 197.6   **8.** 590
9. 2.76   **10.** 5.25   **11.** 9.89   **12.** 4.32   **13.** 18.48   **14.** 47.85   **15.** 50.88   **16.** 47.25
17. 67.64   **18.** 114.21   **19.** 40.608   **20.** 13.944   **21.** 1.792   **22.** 2.584   **23.** 0.0455   **24.** 0.1224

Page 67   ***Exercise 5M***

1. 50   **2.** 90   **3.** 110   **4.** 60   **5.** 320   **6.** 7   **7.** 9   **8.** 13
9. 300   **10.** 1100   **11.** 400   **12.** 30   **13.** 80   **14.** 5700   **15.** 190   **16.** 42
17. (a) 120   (b) 0.1   (c) 0.01   (d) 2   (e) 120   (f) 0.1   **18.** (a) ÷0.1, ÷100, ÷0.001, ÷0.1
    (b) ÷100, ÷0.1, ÷100, ÷0.01   (c) ÷0.1, ÷0.01, ÷10, ÷100   (d) ÷0.01, ÷10, ÷1000, ÷0.01
19. (a) £0.10   (b) £0.01   (c) 127   (d) 805

Page 68   ***Exercise 5E***

1. 7.3   **2.** 6.3   **3.** 3.14   **4.** 3.56   **5.** 0.75   **6.** 0.87   **7.** 32.7   **8.** 3.24
9. 3.42   **10.** 5.7   **11.** 8.3   **12.** 7.2   **13.** 41.6   **14.** 33.7   **15.** 1.423   **16.** 0.65
17. 5.14   **18.** 23.4   **19.** 0.67   **20.** 65   **21.** 14   **22.** 704.1   **23.** 163.8   **24.** 219
25. 3.31   **26.** 1.75   **27.** 420   **28.** 18.8   **29.** 2003   **30.** 87   **31.** 180   **32.** 80
33. 5   **34.** (a) 250   (b) 0.7 pence   **35.** (a) 24.7   (b) 0.0247   (c) 24.7   (d) 2470

Page 69   ***Exercise 6E***

IT IS LONELY ON THE MOON

Page 70   ***Exercise 1M***

1. (a) 80   (b) 800   (c) 80000   (d) 800   (e) 210   (f) 21000
    (g) 150   (h) 15000   (i) 2500   (j) 32000   (k) 24000   (l) 1800
2. (a) 500   (b) 400   (c) 1400   (d) 2000   (e) 3000   (f) 300
    (g) 100   (h) 60   **3.** €50   **4.** (a) 0.6   (b) 0.06   (c) 4.8
    (d) 0.48   (e) 0.8   (f) 0.08   (g) 0.048   (h) 800 000
5. (a) C   (b) B   (c) B   (d) A   (e) B   (f) C   (g) A   (h) C
    (i) B   (j) C   (k) C   (l) C   (m) A   (n) B   (o) B   (p) A
    (q) A   (r) B   (s) A   (t) B   **6.** (a) true   (b) false   (c) true
7. (a) The author's boots have a capacity of 6 litres. One tin of beans has a capacity of about 380 ml.
    About 15 tins are required. (b) £7 → £8

Page 73   ***Exercise 1E***

1. 1 kg   **2.** £700   **3.** £280   **4.** £5000   **5.** £250   **6.** $50 000
7. (a) 35.99   (b) 3.96   (c) 316.8   (d) 15.59   (e) 198   (f) 103.5
8. (a) 20.56   (b) 0.114   (c) 1.23   (d) 98.6   (e) 198.9   (f) 50.76
9. (a) 95.72   (b) 3.124   (c) 183.1   (d) 56.0   (e) 1.00   (f) 31.40

10. £2400 **11.** (a) (i) £32 (ii) £24 (b) (i) £31.45 (ii) £25.96

12. (a) $4300 \times 1000 \div 1.5 \approx 3\,000\,000$ (b) $40\,000 \times 1000 \div 1.5 \approx 27\,000\,000$

13. (a) $80\,000 \to 100\,000$ (b) 0.1 mm **14.** (a) 120 (b) 30 (c) £500

(d) 800 (e) 400 m (f) 10

Page 74 Exercise 2M

1. (a) 1670 (b) 90.8 (c) 32.6 (d) 5.2915 (e) 44.7 **2.** (a) smaller (b) larger

(c) smaller **3.** (a) > (b) < (c) < (d) > **4.** (a) highly unlikely (b) OK

(c) highly unlikely (d) highly unlikely (e) impossible (f) impossible

5. (a) about 8 m (b) £10000 (c) about 70 miles (or 110 km)

Page 76 Exercise 2E

1. (a) 8.2 (b) 7.2 (c) 0.8 (d) 11.3 (e) 0.4 (f) 8.7 (g) 11.5 (h) 0.6

2. (a) 1.25 (b) 8.04 (c) 11.22 (d) 3.08 (e) 0.14 (f) 22.46 (g) 0.86 (h) 6.10

3. (a) 1.60 (b) 4.37 (c) 19.70 (d) 0.89 (e) 3.61 (f) 2.92 (g) 1.85 (h) 0.94

(i) 0.60 (j) 0.91 (k) 1.72 (l) 3.83 **4.** 16.7 cm^2 (accept $16.5 \to 16.9$)

5. (a) 1700 (b) 22500 (c) 800 (d) 15300 (e) 600 (f) 2200 (g) 3600 (h) 1000

6. (a) 26 (b) 3 (c) 21 (d) 10 (e) 8 (f) 5 (g) 17 (h) 13

(i) 14 (j) 9 (k) 4 (l) 26

Page 78 Check Yourself Sections 2.1 and 2.2

1. (a) 1480 (b) 22.172 (c) 638 (d) 7613 (e) 0.162 **2.** (a) 1.9 (b) 0.07

(c) 12 (d) 21.6 (e) 0.0096 (f) 22.4 **3.** (a) (i) 800 (ii) 1200 (iii) 200

(iv) 180 (v) £600 (vi) 30 (b) 2500 km (c) (i) 16.4 (ii) 8.5 (iii) 0.3

Page 79 Exercise 1M

1. $a = 64°$ **2.** $b = 95°$ **3.** $c = 50°$ **4.** $d = 85°, e = 95°$ **5.** $a = 82°, b = 100°$ **6.** $c = 66°$

7. $x = 80°$ **8.** $b = 28°$ **9.** $y = 68°$ **10.** $x = 91°$ **11.** $c = 30°$ **12.** $d = 135°$ **13.** $b = 120°$

14. $c = 40°$ **15.** $x = 105°, y = 80°$ **16.** $a = 20°$ **17.** $b = 40°$ **18.** $c = 24°$ **19.** $d = 68°, e = 115°$

20. $f = 90°, g = 30°$ **21.** $h = 65°$ **22.** $i = 72°$ **23.** $j = 46°$ **24.** $k = 14°$

Page 81 Exercise 1E

1. 40° **2.** 20° **3.** 48° **4.** 102° **5.** 114° **6.** 150° **7.** (b) 36°, 36°, 108°

Page 82 Exercise 2M

1. 72° **2.** 53° **3.** 54° **4.** 26° **5.** 60° **6.** 20° **7.** 52.9° **8.** 63° **9.** $a = 10°, x = 35°$

Page 84 Exercise 2E

1. $\hat{BAC} = \hat{ACX}, a + b + c = 180°$ **2.** 180°, 180°, 360° **3.** $\hat{ABC} = \hat{BCD}, \hat{BCE} = \hat{CBA} + \hat{BAC}$

Page 86   *Exercise 1M*

1. (a) $8m + 2n$ (b) $6x + 4y$ (c) $8p + q$ (d) $5m$ (e) $a + 2b$ (f) $10e + 5f$

(g) $6w + 3$ (h) $11x + 7$ **2.** (a) $2a - 3$ (b) $22m$ (c) $t + 7r$ (d) $10u$

(e) $3 - 21x$ (f) $2a + 3b + 3c$ (g) $20 - a + b$ (h) $13b + 7$

3. A equation,   B expression,   C equation,   D formula,   E expression,   F equation,   G expression,
H expression,   I formula

4. $A - E, B - F, C - D$ **5.** (a) $2a + 8$ (b) $5m + 10$ (c) $6x + 3$ (d) $3x + 3y$

(e) $6w - 18$ (f) $7p - 21$ (g) $12a - 6$ (h) $10x - 10$ (i) $6a + 12b$

6. (a) $7a - 1$ (b) $10x + 4$ (c) $19x + 3$ (d) $8x + 4y + 2$ (e) $2a + 7b - 9$

(f) $13a - 17b + 13c$ **7.** (a) $4n + 4$ (b) $5(a - 2)$ (c) $3(a + 2b)$ (d) $7(x - 4)$

8. (b) and (c)   **9.** (a) $6a - 3$ (b) $8m + 9n + 2$ (c) $7a + 2b + 3$

Page 87   *Exercise 1E*

1. F   **2.** T   **3.** T   **4.** F   **5.** T   **6.** F   **7.** F   **8.** F   **9.** T   **10.** F   **11.** T   **12.** T

13. F   **14.** T   **15.** T   **16.** (a) $n + n, 3n - n$ (b) n^3 (c) $2 \div n$ (d) various answers

17. (a)   (b)   (c)

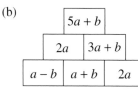 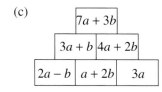

18. (a)   (b)   (c)

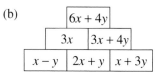 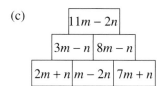

(d)   (e)

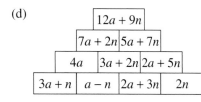 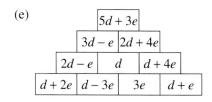

19. (a)   (b)

Page 89   *Exercise 2M*

2.

8	9
9	10

3.

$x - 1$	x
x	$x + 1$

$x - 2$	$x - 1$
$x - 1$	x

$x - 1$	x
x	$x + 1$

4.

x	$x+1$	$x+2$
$x+1$	$x+2$	$x+3$
$x+2$	$x+3$	$x+4$

$x-2$	$x-1$	x
$x-1$	x	$x+1$
x	$x+1$	$x+2$

$x-2$	$x-1$	x
$x-1$	x	$x+1$
x	$x+1$	$x+2$

5.

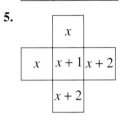

	$y-1$	
	y	
$y+1$	$y+2$	$y+3$

	$z-2$	
	$z-1$	
$z-1$	z	$z+1$

$t-1$	t	$t+1$
t		$t+2$
$t+1$		

Page 90   *Exercise 2E*

1. $5n+x$ **2.** $5(n+x)$ **3.** $6h-t$ **4.** $6(h-t)$ **5.** $5(b+x)$ **6.** $ba+x$

7. $3y^2$ **8.** $dn-3$ **9.** $5(h-H)$ **10.** $5(x-8)$ **11.** $2a+A$ **12.** $2y-3$

13. x^2+2 **14.** $(a+10)^2$ **15.** (a) $5(2n-4)$ (b) $3(5n+7)$ (c) $5(n+2)-3$ (d) $4\left(\dfrac{n}{2}+6\right)$

(e) $8(n^2+7)$ (f) $6(n+3)^2$ **16.** (a) $\times2, +7$ (b) $\times5, -3, \times3$ (c) $\times6, +1, \div5$

(d) square, -3 (e) $+5$, square   (f) square, $-1, \times3$ **17.** square, $\times3, -1, \div5, +7, \times2, +100$

18. 1   **19.** 5   **20.** n **21.** n^2 **22.** $2a+b+c$ **23.** $4m-3$ **24.** $2pq$ **25.** n^2

26. 3   **27.** $2x$ **28.** $\dfrac{1}{a}$ **29.** n **30.** 1   **31.** n **32.** a^3

Page 91   *Exercise 3M*

1. (a) $3n+5$ (b) $2n+6$ (c) $n+3, 3n+9$ (d) 46   **2.** $5x-7$ **3.** $5y-9$ **4.** £$7(d+6)$

5. nt kg   **6.** (a) $(nm+yx+tz)$kg   (b) $(vx+8z+pm)$kg   **7.** $\dfrac{x}{t}$ metres, $\dfrac{nx}{t}$ metres   **8.** $n(z+x)$ **9.** $xy+6$

Page 93   *Exercise 3E*

1. (a) $3n-4$ (b) $3(n-1)$ (c) $3n-4$ (d) $3n-9$ **2.** $b+5, 2a+1; 2d+8, 2c-2$

3. (a) $5^2=4^2+4+5$ (b) $n^2=(n-1)^2+(n-1)+n$ **4.** (a) $5^2=4\times6+1$ (b) $n^2=(n-1)(n+1)+1$

5. $k=2n-1$ **6.** $2[5(x+3)-7]-6\equiv10x+10$

7. (a)

7	2	9
8	6	4
3	10	5

(b)

9	1	8
5	6	7
4	11	3

(c)

8	1	6
3	5	7
4	9	2

(d)

1	12	7	14
8	13	2	11
10	3	16	5
15	6	9	4

(e)

3	10	12	17
14	15	5	8
9	4	18	11
16	13	7	6

8. (a)

$9+6a$	$4-4a$	$5+a$
$2-4a$	$6+a$	$10+6a$
$7+a$	$8+6a$	$3-4a$

(b)

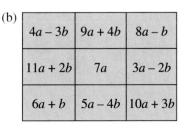

$4a-3b$	$9a+4b$	$8a-b$
$11a+2b$	$7a$	$3a-2b$
$6a+b$	$5a-4b$	$10a+3b$

Page 95   **Check Yourself Sections 2.3 and 2.4**

1. (a) 142°   (b) $b = 106°$, $c = 78°$ (c) $d = 40°$, $e = 60°$ (d) $x = 26°$ (e) $p = 68°$, $q = 56°$, $r = 68°$

2. (a) $4n - 6$ (b) $4c - 2$ (c) $3n^2 - 2n$ (d) $3xy$ (e) m^3 (f) $6e^2$ (g) n (h) t (i) $\frac{3}{m}$

Page 96   **Exercise 1M**

1. (a) F   (b) T   (c) F   (d) F   (e) T   (f) T   **2.** 12 minutes   **3.** 11

4. (a) 10   (b) 20   (c) 0.15   (d) 51   (e) 0.3   (f) 0.02   **5.** (a) 0.8 g   (b) 40

6. (a) 0.35   (b) 0.15   (c) 9.5   (d) 1.23   (e) 1.34   (f) 0.07   **7.** (a) +3   (b) –6

   (c) –6   **8.** 400   **9.** (a) 4 inches   (b) 800 g   (c) 2 m   **10.** (a) 36   (b) 18   (c) 18

Page 98   **Exercise 2M**

1. (a) 33   (b) 1000   (c) 100   (d) 3   (e) 11   (f) 5

2. (a) 35, 70   (b) 30, 70, 80   (c) 12, 18, 30, 51   **3.** 183   **4.** (a) 150   (b) 4.2

5. (a) 0.23   (b) 0.375   (c) £770   **6.** (a) (i) 49   (ii) 72   (iii) 794   (iv) 7249   (b) 9427

7. 12600 seconds = $3\frac{1}{2}$ hours   **8.** (a) 99.5   (b) 22 101 000   (c) 12500   (d) 0.2

9. (a) $32 \div 5 \times 10 = 64$ (b) $99 \times 2 + 2 = 200$ **10.** 1/1/3111

Page 99   **Exercise 3M**

1. (a) 15   (b) –17   (c) 16   (d) –8   (e) –21   (f) –11   (g) 6   (h) –24

   (i) –8   (j) 28   (k) 43   **2.** £162 000   **3.** (a) 1 hour   (b) 3 hours   (c) 2 minutes

4. 1600   **5.** 26.4 cm   **6.** £2 500 000 000   **7.** 10   **8.** 0.7 seconds   **9.** 12 km   **10.** 6

Page 101   **Exercise 4M**

1. 31   **2.** (a) $674 + 382 + 819 = 1875$ (b) $2073 + 1562 + 4582 = 8217$ **3.** 88 km

4. (a) $3 \times 27p$ (b) $(2 \times 36p) + (3 \times 27p)$ (c) $(2 \times 36p) + (5 \times 27p)$ or $(5 \times 36p) + (1 \times 27p)$

5. €64500   **6.** $55\sqrt{5}$ **7.** 100 cm²   **8.** (a) $\dfrac{9 + 9}{9}$ (b) $\dfrac{77}{7}$ (c) $5 + \left(\dfrac{5 + 5}{5}\right)$

   (d) $5 + \dfrac{5}{5}$ (e) $8 \div \left(\dfrac{8 + 8}{8}\right)$ **9.** 26   **10.** £12.25

Page 102   **Exercise 5E**

1. 595 g   **2.** (a) 65   (b) 0.149   (c) $\dfrac{1}{13}$ **3.** (a) $16\frac{2}{3}$ m/s   (b) $3\frac{1}{3}$ m/s/s

4. (a) 40   (b) 70   **5.** 755 g   **6.** (a)

278	311	589
68	257	325
346	568	914

   (b) 47.2%

7. £4.50   **8.** (a) T   (b) T   (c) T   **9.** (a) $59\frac{1}{4}$

   (d) F   (e) F   (f) T

   (b) $56\frac{1}{2}$ (c) $3\frac{1}{5}$ (d) $1\frac{19}{100}$

   (e) $23\frac{9}{10}$ (f) $4\frac{3}{4}$ (g) $5\frac{1}{10}$ (h) $50\frac{2}{5}$

10.      Two pieces like this.

Page 104   **Exercise 6E**

1. 2500 km   **2.** (a) 5, 37, 323   (b) 529   (c) 8   (d) 296 = 8 × 37   **3.** 68%   **4.** (a) 2.5

   (b) 2   **5.** (a) 158 cm²   (b) 316   **6.** (d) 2   **7.** (b) 0.003500035   (c) 0.00035000035

8. 333   **9.** (a) £301.76   (b) £312.08   **10.** (a) 2.3636   (b) 0.2694

Page 107   **Exercise 1M**

1. 40.8 cm   **2.** 18.8 cm   **3.** 50.3 cm   **4.** 15.4 cm   **5.** 20.1 cm   **6.** 72.3 m

7. 45.9 cm   **8.** 56.5 m   **9.** circle by 1.4 cm   **10.** 59.7 mm   **11.** 50.3 cm   **12.** 502.7 cm

13. Tennis ball further by 86 cm   **14.** (a) 28 cm   (b) 22.0 cm

Page 108   **Exercise 1E**

1. 735 m   **2.** 24.6 cm   **3.** 6   **4.** 60   **5.** 408 seconds   **6.** (a) 232 cm

   (b) 860   **7.** 318 mm   **8.** (a) 174 m   (b) 308   **9.** 372 cm   **10.** 253 km

Page 110   **Exercise 2M**

1. 28.3 cm   **2.** 38.6 cm   **3.** 21.9 cm   **4.** 24.0 cm   **5.** 28.1 cm   **6.** 19.4 cm

7. 34.7 cm   **8.** 36.6 cm   **9.** 25.0 cm   **10.** 25.7 cm   **11.** 18.8 cm   **12.** 15.7 cm

Page 111   **Exercise 3M**

1. 154 cm²   **2.** 78.5 cm²   **3.** 573 m²   **4.** 30.2 m²   **5.** 60.8 km²   **6.** 0.503 km²

7. 70.9 cm²   **8.** 24.6 m²   **9.** 38.5 km²   **10.** 9   **11.** 25.1 cm²   **12.** 109 cm²

13. 19.6 cm²   **14.** 73.5 cm²   **15.** 804.2 cm²

Page 113   **Exercise 3E**

1. 13.2 m²   **2.** 16.5 cm²   **3.** 13.7 cm²   **4.** 25.9 cm²   **5.** 42.9 cm²   **6.** 42.1 cm²

7. 28.3 cm²   **8.** 0.858 cm²   **9.** (a) 2.54 m²   (b) Antarctica   **10.** 35.3 cm²   **11.** 17.4 m²

12. 1829   **13.** 9.55 cm

Page 114   **Check Yourself or Section 2.7**

1. (a) 32.7 cm   (b) 19.4 cm   (c) 28.6 cm   **2.** (a) 84.9 cm²   (b) 26.1 cm²   (c) 50.3 cm²

Page 115   **Unit 2 Mixed Review**

Part one

1. (a) 92°   (b) $b = 84°$, $c = 96°$ (c) $x = 35°$ **2.** 3:44   **3.** (a) 2608   (b) 2135   (c) 235

   (d) 2.22 (e) 282   (f) 0.042   **4.** 1st column: 4, −5, −1, 2, 8; 2nd column: −12, 15, 3, −6, −24

5. £10 800   **6.** (a) 19.9   (b) 0.97   (c) 48.0   (d) 99.8   (e) 0.11   (f) 211.2

7. (a) 37.7 cm   (b) 50.3 m   (c) 18.8 cm   **8.** $a = 24°$, $x = 26°$ **9.** (a) 0.4   (b) 7.8   (c) 1.7

   (d) 17.6   (e) 2.03   (f) 0.04   (g) 4.4   (h) 0.43   (i) 0.75

10. 25.1 cm²   **11.** (a) $\frac{23}{40}$ (b) 28.5   (c) 18.03   (d) −8   (e) 200

Part two

1. 1200 g   2. (a) 8.721   (b) 19.95   (c) 12.649   (d) 3.27   3. (a) 5000
   (b) 10   (c) 100   (d) 20   (e) £20   4. (a) 75.4 cm^2 (b) 70.7 cm^2
5. (a) 4.25   (b) 32.5   (c) 0.45   (d) 0.8   (e) 2.45   (f) 11.6
   (g) 0.28   (h) 3.14   (i) 0.3255   6. $(5\pi + 10)$ cm   7. £360.52   8. 23 minutes
9. (a) $a = 65°, b = 44°, c = 65°$ (b) $a = 36°$, angles 144°, 69°, 75°   10. (a) 20.28   (b) 100.94
   (c) 9.24   (d) 0.2   (e) 200   (f) 2.97   11. 3.9 kg   12. 152.7×2.01
13. $x = 4.69$ cm, $r = 2.65$ cm

Page 119   **Puzzles and Problems 2**

1. OH   2. SIGHED   3. DEBBIE   4. BED   5. SID   6. BOB
7. SID   8. BOB   9. DOGS   10. DIG   11. SOIL   12. BIG
13. BODIES   14. LODGE   15. HILL   16. OH   17. GOOD   18. DEBBIE
19. BESSIE   20. SELL   21. GOOSE   22. EGGS   23. HELLO   24. DEBBIE
25. OH   26. SHE   27. GIGGLED   28. SHOES   29. DEBBIE   30. EGGS
31. SHE   32. HELD   33. BOIL   34. DEBBIE   35. BESSIE   36. EDIBLE
37. BOSS   38. SHELL   39. HE DIED   40. SOLD
41. ELSE (Question error should be $60^2 - 3^3$ Apologies)   42. OH I SEE   43. BOILED
44. EGGS   45. SHED   46. BESSIE   47. DEBBIES   48. HOBBIES   49. BIDE
50. HEDGEHOG   51. DOGS   52. LOOSE   53. BESSIE   54. HEELED   55. SHOES
56. SHE   57. SIGHED   58. HOLES   59. HOLD   60. EGGS
61. (Error, delete this clue)   62. BESSIE   63. GOOD BYE   64. DODGE

Page 121   **Mental Arithmetic Practice**

1. $\frac{3}{4}$ 2. true   3. 45p   4. One million   5. 26   6. 45 miles
7. £50   8. 0.3   9. 1900 ml   10. 3 h 45 min   11. 20   12. £7
13. 50p, 2p, 1p   14. 1800   15. £4.40   16. north   17. 7.50   18. 95.1
19. 1st of October   20. 23   21. 90%   22. 40%   23. 63 kg   24. 6 cm^2
25. 165   26. 1.7   27. 1.7 cm   28. 7 cm   29. £80   30. true

Page 122   **A long time ago! 2**

1. (a) 5   (b) 3   (c) 6   (d) 9   (e) 2   (f) 10
   (g) 12   (h) 15   2. 16   3. 100000   4. 1000000
5. (a) 10001   (b) 11000   (c) 100   (d) 1110   (e) 101100
6. (a) 1000   (b) 10100   (c) 11001   7. (a) 110   (b) 101   (c) 1100

Unit 3

Page 127   **Exercise 2M**

5. (e) $(-2, 4), (-6, 4), (-4, 6), (-3, 6)$ **6.** (e) $(1, 4), (-1, 3), (2, 3), (2, 4)$

7. (a) $y = -1$ (b) $x = 3$ (c) $y = x$ (d) $y = 0$ (e) $y = -x$

Page 129   **Exercise 2E**

1. (e) $y = -x$ **2.** (e) $y = -\frac{1}{2}$

4. (a) ꟻꓭAИƆƎ (France)   (b) ИOꙄ⅃ƎИ (Nelson)   (c) ИOTWƎИ (Newton)   **5.** ƎƆИA⅃UꓭMA

6. The three images of P should lie on a straight line.

7. (a) (i) $(9, 6)$ (ii) $(99, 6)$ (iii) $(1, -2)$ (iv) $(1, 394)$ (v) $(6, 1)$ (vi) $(-6, -1)$

  (b) (i) $(207, 63)$ (ii) $(-207, -63)$ (c) $(a, -b)$ (d) $(-a, b)$ **8.** $y = 2, y = 2\frac{1}{2}, x + y = 5, y = x$

Page 130   **Two reflections**

Mirror lines are always 6 units apart.

Page 132   **Exercise 1M**

1. (a) 4.6   (b) 7   (c) 3   (d) 23   **2.** (a) 7   (b) 6   (c) 10

3. (a) $0 - 17, 1 - 9, 2 - 14, 3 - 14, 4 - 13, 5 - 15, 6 - 17, 7 - 12, 8 - 20, 9 - 17$

  (b) 14.5   (c) 75p   **4.** £3.99   **5.** (a) 1.50 m   (b) 1.482 m

6. $-1°$ C   **7.** 6   **8.** (a) 34.1 years   (b) 55.1 years

9. (a) 27   (b) 91   (c) 12   **10.** 9   **11.** 9

Page 133   **Exercise 1E**

  1. 5 and 9   **2.** mean = 17, median = 3. The median is more representative

  3. (a) 1.74 m   (b) 1.73 m   **4.** The median   **5.** 1 or 70   **6.** 45, 75

  7. many answers e.g. 4, 4, 6, 10, 11   **8.** 13   **9.** Tom: 50, 60, 70   **10.** 15, 20, 31

11. (a) (i) $4x + 2$ (ii) $x + 6$ (iii) $2x + 3$ (b) 5

12. (a) (i) n (ii) $n - 2$ (iii) $\frac{4n - 3}{3}$ (b) $n = 12$, mean = 15   **13.** $\dfrac{nh - x + y}{n}$

Page 135   **Exercise 2M**

1. (a) 1.601 m, 0.07 m   (b) 1.518 m, 0.29 m

  (c) The children in school A were taller than in school B and their heights
     were less spread out than in school B. [or similar]

2. (a) mean = 83.875 kg, range = 36 kg   (c) More young tigers perhaps?

3. Red ants: median 13, range 23. Black ants: median 13, range 9

4. (a) 4   (b) In Luton there were more houses with several people in them.

  (b) In Stevenage there may be more old people living on their own.

     (Any reasonable answer is acceptable.)

Page 137   **Exercise 2E**

1. 51.9 g   **2.** 96.25 g   **3.** 51.9p   **4.** (a) 6.52   (b) 6   (c) 5

5. (a) mean = 5.3, median = 5, mode 4   (b) For discussion (any reasoned argument is acceptable)

6. 6.7 g   **7.** (a) 38   (b) 16   (c) 11   **8.** 6×6 g, 7×7 g

Page 139   **Exercise 3M**

3. (a) 49 kg   (b) 17   (c) 51 kg   **4.** (a) 4.6   (b) 5.3

Page 140   **Check Yourself Sections 3.3 and 3.4**

1. (b) vertices at: (i) (−3, 1) (−3, 4) (−5, 4)   (ii) (1, 1) (1, −2) (3, −2)

(c) (i) $y = -\dfrac{1}{2}$ (ii) $y = x$ **2.** (a) 11   (b) 5.75 m

Page 141   **Exercise 1M**

A	**1.** 69	**2.** 87	**3.** 87	**4.** 115	**5.** 97	**6.** 179
	7. 98	**8.** 107	**9.** 106	**10.** 65	**11.** 69	**12.** 154
B	**1.** 58	**2.** 88	**3.** 81	**4.** 101	**5.** 116	**6.** 94
	7. 166	**8.** 157	**9.** 137	**10.** 187	**11.** 113	**12.** 137
C	**1.** 74	**2.** 103	**3.** 96	**4.** 86	**5.** 68	**3.** 103
	7. 86	**8.** 65	**9.** 15	**10.** 32	**11.** 58	**12.** 32

Page 143   **Exercise 1E**

D	**1.** 108	**2.** 76	**3.** 134	**4.** 146	**5.** 56	**6.** 158
	7. 230	**8.** 252	**9.** 174	**10.** 132	**11.** 474	**12.** 684
E	**1.** 1100	**2.** 1600	**3.** 600	**4.** 400	**5.** 280	**6.** 120
	7. 315	**8.** 315	**9.** 700	**10.** 260	**11.** 900	**12.** 300
F	**1.** 147	**2.** 459	**3.** 451	**4.** 713	**5.** 171	**6.** 174
	7. 693	**8.** 1485	**9.** 1212	**10.** 5555	**11.** 23 023	**12.** 14 985

Page 143   **KS3 Tests**

Test 1

1. 20	**2.** 14 cm	**3.** 7	**4.** 4	**5.** $\dfrac{2}{3}$
6. 0.8	**7.** 30	**8.** 7.40	**9.** 60	**10.** $\dfrac{3}{5}$
11. 13	**12.** 80	**13.** 5	**14.** 2 500 000	**15.** 66
16. 45°	**17.** £8–£9	**18.** 9	**19.** 455	**20.** $3(n + 6)$
21. £30	**22.** 50 000	**23.** 17, 18	**24.** 130	**25.** £5.50
26. 400	**27.** 6	**28.** 3	**29.** 144	**30.** 4800

Test 2

1. 1600	**2.** 5200	**3.** 20	**4.** a^3	**5.** 10
6. 50 000	**7.** 10	**8.** 1.71 m	**9.** 55	**10.** 50°
11. 35	**12.** 28 cm²	**13.** 32	**14.** 20	**15.** 60%
16. 100	**17.** various	**18.** 9	**19.** 6020	**20.** 4
21. £8.97	**22.** 0.18	**23.** 250	**24.** 128 cm	**25.** 5, 6
26. 304	**27.** 800 m	**28.** −6	**29.** triangle	**30.** 11.05

Test 1 Answer sheet

Time: 5 seconds

Question	Answer	
1		18 22
2	cm	
3		
4		$3n = 12$
5		$\frac{14}{21}$
6		

Time: 10 seconds

7		$5x$
8		
9		
10		50 pupils, 30 girls
11		$32 - (12 + 7)$
12		
13	m	
14		
15		$x - 3 = 30$
16		
17		52% £16.90
18		
19		
20		

Time: 15 seconds

21		1:2 £15
22		
23		
24		$17 \times 260 = 4420$, 2210
25		£22 4
26		41.22×9.87
27		
28		1, 3, 4, 4
29		$(3 + 4 + 5)^2$
30		

Test 2 Answer sheet

Time: 5 seconds

Question	Answer	
1		1567
2		5.2
3		
4		$a \times a \times a$
5		2.3 2.7 2.3 2.7
6		

Time: 10 seconds

7		$2(x + 1)$
8		1.7m $\frac{1}{100}$ m
9		
10		
11		
12	cm²	
13	m	$4x + y$ $8x + 2y$
14		2 0.1
15	%	
16		$(1 + 2 + 3 + 4)^2$
17		$-4 < x < 0$
18		
19		6.02
20		$3 \times \boxed{} - 1 = 65$

Time: 15 seconds

21	£	
22	0.3 0.18	0.35 0.332 0.2
23		$497.3 \div 1.97$
24		
25		3, 4 4, 5 5, 6 6, 7 7, 8
26		$32 \times 19 = 608$
27		1:10000 8 cm
28		$(x - 3)(x + 2)$
29		
30		8.50 pm $2\frac{1}{4}$

Page 147   **Exercise 1M**

1. 14   **2.** 21   **3.** 6   **4.** 0   **5.** 55   **6.** 32   **7.** 11

8. 6   **9.** 83   **10.** 3   **11.** £75 000   **12.** 3   **13.** 12   **14.** 26

15. −5   **16.** 0.5   **17.** 33

Page 147   **Exercise 1E**

1. (a) 49   (b) 9   (c) 27   **2.** (a) 23   (b) 5   (c) 17

3. 0.33   **4.** (a) 127   (b) 52   (c) 86   **5.** (a) −100   (b) 8

6. (a) 720°   (c) 18 000°   **7.** (a) 55   (b) 4950   **8.** (b) 220

9. (a) 600   (b) 300   **10.** (a) 2   (b) 15   (c) 21   (d) 9

11. 0.08002   **12.** (a) 16 km (b) 28.2 m   **13.** $d = n - 3$ **14.** (b) 46   (c) $w = 2b + 6$

Page 151   **Exercise 2M**

1. 9   **2.** 5   **3.** 13   **4.** 15   **5.** 15   **6.** 3

7. 6   **8.** 19   **9.** 22   **10.** 6   **11.** (b), (c), (f) are false

12. (a) 8   (b) 18   (c) 27   **13.** (a) 8   (b) 4.5   (c) 1.5

14. (a) 2   (b) 6   (c) $4\frac{1}{2}$ **15.** (a) 3   (b) −6   (c) −3   (d) −10

      (e) 8   (f) 4   **16.** $2n^2, \quad \left(\dfrac{4}{n} + n\right)^2 \div n, \quad 12 - n^2$

Page 152   **Exercise 2E**

1. 0   **2.** 8   **3.** 6   **4.** 1   **5.** 2   **6.** −3

7. 8   **8.** 16   **9.** 4   **10.** 0   **11.** 24   **12.** 13

13. 3   **14.** −1   **15.** 17   **16.** −9   **17.** 30   **18.** 10

19. 3   **20.** −3   **21.** 45   **22.** 23   **23.** 41   **24.** 9

25. 4   **26.** 8   **27.** 21   **28.** −12   **29.** 14   **30.** 27

31. −7   **32.** 8   **33.** 9   **34.** 25

35. All except $2^3 + n^3 + n$ and $(2n + 1)^2 - 4n^2$

36. (a) 8   (b) 25   (c) 13   (d) 13   (e) 0   (f) 35

37. (a) 1   (b) −7   (c) 9   (d) −6   (e) 2   (f) −22

38. (a) 37   (b) 2   (c) 36   (d) 6   (e) −35   (f) −168

Page 154   **Check Yourself Section 3.3 and 3.4**

1. (a) 1600   (b) 120   (c) 78   (d) 103   (e) 178   (f) 217

   (g) 4545   (h) 1400   (i) 0.26   (j) 150°   (k) £10.50

2. (a) (i) 25   (ii) 53   (iii) 58   (b) (i) 5   (ii) 30   (iii) 23   (iv) −40

   (c) $\dfrac{4n}{n}, \dfrac{12}{n}, 10^n - 996, \dfrac{(n + 1)^2}{4}$

Page 155 **Exercise 1M**

1. 7.5 cm   **2.** 7.0 cm   **3.** 33°   **4.** $78\frac{1}{2}°$ **5.** $104\frac{1}{2}°$ **6.** 8.0 cm   **7.** 99°   **8.** 81°   **9.** 9.0 cm

Page 156 **Exercise 2M**

1. A circle, centre C   **3.** A line which bisects the right angle.
4. (a) A full circle   (b) A semicircle   **5.** Five full circles

Page 157 **Exercise 2E**

1. All points inside and on a circle of radius 2 cm, centre O.   **2.** (b) 12.00
3. Up 1, turn right, ahead 2 units, turn right, ahead 3 units etc.   **5.** lines $y = x$ and $y = -x$
6. (a) clockwise   (b) anti-clockwise   (c) clockwise

Page 158 **Exercise 3M**

6. Angles in triangle ABC are the same as angles in triangle PQR.

Page 159 **Exercise 3E**

7. All 3 lines pass through one point.

Page 161 **Unit 3 Mixed Review**

Part one

1. (a) 0.13   (b) 1000   (c) 8.67   (d) 12.4   (e) 5.28   (f) 1280
2. (a) 3.99, 4.03   (b) 4.95, 5, 5.15   **3.** (a) F   (b) T   (c) T   (d) T
    (e) T   (f) T   **4.** (a) 40p   (b) $(100 - 10n)$ pence   **5.** 67.5
6. (a) $(19 + 16) \times 7 = 245$ (b) $(13 - 4) \times (4 + 3) = 63$ (c) $7 \times (4.15 + 2.3) = 45.15$
    (d) $19 \times 5 - 2 = 3 \times (14 + 17)$ **7.** 3.6   **8.** (a) 76   (b) 39   (c) 88
    (d) 134   (e) 1200   (f) 550   (g) 272   (h) 103   **9.** 52
10. $A = \dfrac{b \times h}{2}$ **11.** 141   **12.** £419 750   **13.** (a) $6^2 = 5^2 + (2 \times 5) + 1$
    (b) $n^2 = (n - 1)^2 + 2(n - 1) + 1$ **15.** 100 000 000   **16.** 211

Part two

1. $x = 3$ **3.** points on the line $y = x$ **4.** 8.82   **5.** (a) 8   (b) 12   (c) 81
    (d) 3   (e) 15   (f) 12   **6.** (a) 6   (b) –6   (c) 0
    (d) 4   (e) –12   (f) 0   **7.** (a) 23.9 pence   (b) 5 pence   **8.** 1
9. 1122   **10.** (a) 53   (b) 45   **11.** 15.2 kg   **12.** 1500   **13.** (a) 15
    (b) 30   (c) 25   (d) 25   **14.** (a) (i) T   (ii) T   (iii) F
    (iv) T   (b) (i) $2g$ (ii) y (iii) y (iv) g
18. It was Italy (but Greece is acceptable).   **19.** (a) (iv) 7.3 – 7.4 cm   (b) circle radius 5 cm, centre Q

Page 166　　**Puzzles and Problems 3**

Hidden words

1. His glue does not stick

2. Beavers cut down trees

3. Soleil is sun in French

4. My cat chases only mice

Page 167　　**Break the codes**

1. $\odot = 6$, $\nabla = 3$, $\square = 7$, $* = 1$, $\uparrow = 0$, $? = 2$, $\ominus = 9$, $\pi = 5$, $\mp = 8$, $I = 4$.

2. $\odot = 4$, $\nabla = 6$, $\square = 1$, $* = 3$, $\uparrow = 9$, $? = 0$, $\ominus = 5$, $\pi = 8$, $\mp = 2$, $I = 7$.

3. $* = 1$, $\ominus = 2$, $\odot = 3$, $\nabla = 4$, $\pi = 5$, $\mp = 6$, $\uparrow = 7$, $\square = 8$, $? = 9$

Page 168　　**Mental Arithmetic Pratice**

1. £9.65	**2.** 23 min	**3.** 4 cm	**4.** 12.5%	**5.** 61	**6.** 13.5 cm
7. True	**8.** 18.30	**9.** 10	**10.** 1 m^2	**11.** $\frac{1}{9}$	**12.** 14p
13. 21	**14.** 10 km	**15.** 16	**16.** 13	**17.** £2	**18.** 100°
19. ~150	**20.** 35	**21.** £15	**22.** 18th July	**23.** $\frac{1}{50}$	**24.** $\frac{3}{8}$
25. £9	**26.** 10	**27.** £2.75	**28.** 12 square units	**29.** 3600	**30.** 120 mph

Page 170　　**A long time ago! 3**

1. 1, 1, 2, 3, 5, 8, 13, 21, 34, 55, 89, 144, 233, 377, 610, 987, 1597, 2584, 4181, 6765, 10946, 17711.

2. (a) GGGG, BGGG, GBGG, GGBG, GGGB, BGBG, BGGB, GBGB

(b) GGGGG, BGGGG, GBGGG, GGBGG, GGGBG, GGGGB, BGBGG, BGGBG, BGGGB, GBGBG, GBGGB, GGBGB, BGBGB

(c) 144　　(d) 17711

Unit 4

Page 172   Exercise 1M

1. Henry 036°, Jane 061°, Carol 090°, Paul 119°, Wendy 163°, Janet 192°, Terry 214°, Mark 256°, Ann 314°, Stephen 324°.   **2.** G 035°, I 072°, A 085°, C 123°, F 139°, E 180°, B 200°, J 247°, H 280°, D 330°

3. Amy 060°, Ben 034°, Chris 146°, Don 225°, Eloise 270°, Fran 333°   **4.** (a) 054°   (b) 077°   (c) 057°

(d) 108°   (e) 203°   **6.** (a) (6, 5)   (b) (4, 4)   (c) (5, 3)   (d) (5, 7)   (e) (4, 7)

7. 110°, 260°, 130°   **8.** 280°   **9.** 020°

Page 175   Exercise 1E

1. 8.6 km   **2.** 7.7 km   **3.** 11.5 km   **4.** 8.7 km   **5.** 10.7 km   **6.** 077$\frac{1}{2}$° (±2°)   **7.** 9.6 km   **8.** (c) 113°

(d) about 26 km/h.   **9.** 8.8 km on a bearing 022°   **10.** about 211° (±3°)   **11.** Sir Francis

12. (a) 041°   (b) 18 km/h

Page 180   Exercise 1M

2. (a) 3   (b) 12   (c) 7   (d) '....... of drinks sold *decreases*.'   **3.** (a) 7   (b) 6   (c) no

Page 182   Exercise 2M

2. (a) strong positive correlation   (b) no correlation   (c) weak negative correlation

(d) strong negative correlation   **3.** (a) no correlation   (b) strong positive correlation

(c) no correlation   (d) strong negative correlation

Page 183   Exercise 2E

1. (b) About 20   **2.** About 88 g   **3.** positive correlation

4. For discussion   **5.** no correlation   **6.** For discussion

Page 186   Exercise 3M

1. (a) 70%   (b) Yes   (c) 65%   **2.** (a) £40 000   (b) 4   (c) January, February   (d) £140 000

3. (a) England and Wales   (b) about 50   (c) Almost no car theft   (d) Six times as likely

(e) Fewer large cities? For discussion   **4.** Frequencies in order 2 → 12: 3, 5, 5, 9, 11, 15, 7, 1, 5, 6, 3

5. (a) about £360   (b) Mr Brown: about £200; Mrs Evans: about £300.

6. (a) 40%, 10%, 70%   (b) older people prefer cruise holiday to skiing

Page 188   Exercise 3E

1. (a) 6   (b) 5   **2.** angles 70°, 14°; numbers 230, 66, 114, 142   **3.** Angles: 45°, 45°, 54°, 36°, 36°, 144°

4. (a) 72°   (b) 126°   **5.** (a) 20%   (b) $x = 126°, y = 79°$ **6.** (a) £351 (author is Taurus)   **7.** Yes

Page 192   Check Yourself on Units 4.1 and 4.3

1. (a) 045°   (b) 090°   (c) 135°   (d) 180°   (e) 225°   (f) 270°   **2.** (a) (ii) strong negative correlation

(b) A positive, B none, C none, D strong negative

Page 193   ***Exercise 1M***

1. 0.4 **2.** 0.25   **3.** 0.375   **4.** 0.2   **5.** 0.9   **6.** 0.75   **7.** 0.6   **8.** 0.5   **9.** 0.3   **10.** 0.875

11. 1.4   **12.** 4.75   **13.** 3.5   **14.** 1.875   **15.** 5.01   **16.** 0.85, $\frac{7}{8}$, $\frac{9}{10}$ **17.** $\frac{31}{50}$, 0.645, $\frac{13}{20}$

18. 0.715, $\frac{29}{40}$, $\frac{3}{4}$ **19.** 0.18, $\frac{3}{16}$, $\frac{1}{5}$ **20.** (a) $\frac{1}{2}$ (b) $\frac{3}{4}$ (c) $\frac{1}{8}$

Page 195   ***Exercise 1E***

1. $0.\dot{6}$ **2.** $0.\dot{2}$ **3.** $0.\dot{7}$ **4.** $0.1\dot{6}$ **5.** $0.41\dot{6}$ **6.** $0.0\dot{3}$ **7.** $0.2\dot{3}$ **8.** $0.2\dot{6}$ **9.** $0.1\dot{8}$ **10.** $0.4\dot{5}$

11. (a) $\frac{1}{7} = 0.\dot{1}4285\dot{7}$, $\frac{2}{7} = 0.\dot{2}8571\dot{4}$, $\frac{3}{7} = 0.\dot{4}2857\dot{1}$, $\frac{4}{7} = 0.\dot{5}7142\dot{8}$, $\frac{5}{7} = 0.\dot{7}1428\dot{5}$, $\frac{6}{7} = 0.\dot{8}5714\dot{2}$

12. (b) $\frac{1}{13} = 0.\dot{0}7692\dot{3}$, $\frac{4}{13} = 0.\dot{3}0769\dot{2}$, $\frac{9}{13} = 0.\dot{6}9230\dot{7}$ (c) the sequence 076923 occurs each time

Page 195   ***Recurrrrrrinngggg decimals***

1. (b) $\frac{1}{17} = 0.\dot{0}588235294117647\dot{7}$ **2.** $\frac{1}{19} = 0.\dot{0}5263157894736842\dot{1}$

Page 196   ***Exercise 2M***

1. $\frac{2}{5}$ **2.** $\frac{7}{10}$ **3.** $\frac{3}{100}$ **4.** $\frac{1}{20}$ **5.** $\frac{7}{1000}$ **6.** $\frac{3}{500}$ **7.** $\frac{2}{25}$ **8.** $\frac{3}{25}$ **9.** $\frac{19}{50}$

10. $\frac{3}{200}$ **11.** $\frac{1}{4}$ **12.** $\frac{9}{20}$ **13.** $\frac{37}{100}$ **14.** $\frac{1}{40}$ **15.** $\frac{1}{8}$ **16.** (a) $\frac{1}{50}$ (b) $\frac{3}{20}$ (c) $\frac{4}{25}$

Page 197   ***Exercise 3M***

1. 50%   **2.** 75%   **3.** 40%   **4.** 70%   **5.** 65%   **6.** 12.5%   **7.** 62.5%   **8.** 25%   **9.** 35%   **10.** 71%

11. (a) 56%   **12.** 82.5%   (c) 70%   (d) 55%   **12.** 8P = 62.5%, 8W = 60%, 8P highest   **13.** (a) 32%

(b) 14%   (c) 3%   (d) 81.5%   (e) 140%   **14.** (a) 83%   (b) 58%   (c) 44%   (d) 55%   (e) 67%

15. (a) 30%   (b) 35%   (c) 25%   (d) 10%   **16.** (a) 0.6, $\frac{5}{8}$, 66%   (b) 0.056, 55%, $\frac{5}{9}$

(c) $\frac{3}{7}$, $\frac{5}{11}$, $45\frac{1}{2}$%   (d) 0.0005, $\frac{1}{1000}$, 0.2%

Page 197   ***Exercise 3E***

2. (a) RATIOS ARE FUN   (b) GOLF IS MY GAME   (c) HALF OF TEN IS FIVE   **4.** (a) 0.36

(b) 0.67   (c) 0.43   (d) 0.48   (e) 0.33   (f) 0.11   (g) 0.01   **5.** (a) Yes   (b) No

Page 199   ***Exercise 4M***

1. £72   **2.** £15   **3.** £7.29   **4.** £36   **5.** £30.80   **6.** £79.55   **7.** £1.10   **8.** £26.40 **9.** £204.40

10. £340   **11.** £13   **12.** £0.42   **13.** £580   **14.** £18   **15.** £29.75 **16.** 12.6 kg **17.** £2.85 **18.** £0.28

19. £1.58   **20.** £1.19 **21.** £0.69   **22.** £0.80 **23.** £0.14   **24.** £1.92   **25.** £1.68   **26.** £0.03 **27.** £0.53

28. £10.86 **29.** £2.47 **30.** £1.52   **31.** £1.09 **32.** £4.15

Page 200   ***Exercise 4E***

1. £94.50   **2.** £48   **3.** 37.1 m.p.g.   **4.** 18.2 kg   **5.** 21.63 m   **6.** £20.80, £93.60, £67.60

7. 52.8 kg   **8.** 2.673 kg   **9.** 604.8 g   **10.** 59278

Page 201   ***Exercise 5E***

1. (a) 155   (b) 0.37, 888   (c) 12, 5.76   **2.** (a) 26.4 kg   (b) £23.10   (c) $2016   (d) £1650
(e) 33 m   **3.** £604.80   **4.** (a) 1.06   (b) 720   **5.** £83.20   **6.** £260   **7.** £432   **8.** £16.16
9. £2790   **10.** £110.70   **11.** £102   **12.** £7800   **13.** £6630   **14.** £21.69   **15.** $22,200,200
16. £779.22   **17.** €56192.50

Page 203   ***Exercise 1M***

1. D, C, B, A   **2.** 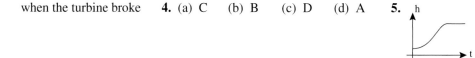   **3.** A → Z, B → Y, C → X

4.    **5.** (a) No   (b) 50 g   (c) Some crisps were bigger than others.

6.   **7.**

8. AB engine on, BC engine off, CD engine on, DE tank filled, EF engine off, FG engine on

Page 205   ***Exercise 1E***

1. (a) 13.30   (b) 15.15 and 15.30   (c) 14.45   (d) (i) 60 km/h   (ii) 40 km/h   (iii) 80 km/h
2. (c) (i) 50 km   (ii) 16.00   **3.** Energy generated increased in a strong wind and then went to zero
when the turbine broke   **4.** (a) C   (b) B   (c) D   (d) A   **5.**

6. (a) (i) 15 km/litre   (ii) 14.5 km/litre   (iii) 5 km/litre   (b) (i) 160 km/h   (ii) 130 km/h
(iii) 153 km/h approximately   (c) about 55 km/h   (d) 160 km   (e) 960 km
7.

Page 207   ***Check Yourself on Sections 4.4 and 4.5***

1. (a) (i) 40%   (ii) 0.02   (iii) 0.$\dot{2}$ (iv) 62%   (b) £21.28   (c) €4.18, £122.93
2. events in order: IJ, BC, JK, CD, DE and/or HI, AB, EF

Page 208   **Exercise 1M**

7. (a) 90° clockwise about centre of puzzle   (b) 180°, same centre

Page 209   **Exercise 1E**

3. (f) 90° clockwise, centre (6, 4)   **4.** (f) 90° clockwise, centre (–3, 5)

5. (a) 77° clockwise about centre   (b) 103° anticlockwise about centre

Page 210   **Exercise 2M**

5. (a) (2, 0)   (b) (0, 0)   (c) (0, –1)   (d) (–3, 3)

Page 211   **Exercise 2E**

1.

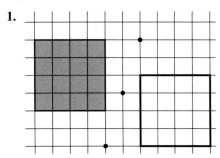

2. (a) Reflection in $y = x$ (b) Rotation 180°, centre (0, –2)

(c) Reflection in $y = -2$ (d) Rotation 90° anticlockwise, centre $(-4\frac{1}{2}, 4\frac{1}{2})$

3. (a) Reflection in $y = x$ (b) Rotation 180°, centre (5, 0)

(c) Rotation 90° clockwise, centre (–2, 2)   (d) Rotation 180°, centre $(\frac{1}{2}, 1\frac{1}{2})$

(e) Reflection in $y = -3\frac{1}{2}$ **4.** (a) translation   (b) reflection   (c) rotation 180°

Page 212   **Exercise 3M**

1. (c) rotation 180° about 0   **2.** (c) rotation 180° about (0, 0)

3. (d) 5 units right, 2 units up

4. (a) rotation 90° clockwise, centre (3, 1)   (b) reflection in $y = 3\frac{1}{2}$

(c) rotation 90° anticlockwise, centre (3, 6)   (d) various [could be (a) then (b)]

5. (a) rotation 90° anticlockwise, centre (0, 0)   (b) reflection in $y = 0$

(c) reflection in $y = x$ (d) translation, 9 units right

(e), (f) various answers

6. (b) mirror lines are always 6 units apart   (c) yes

7. various ways, for example: translation 2 units right, then reflection in $y = 0$ or translation 2 units right, 4 units up and then reflection in $y = 2$

Page 214   **Exercise 3E**

1. triangle 1: rotation 90° clockwise, centre (3, 3) then reflection in $y = 3$

triangle 2: rotation 180°, centre (0, 0) then reflection in $x = -2$

triangle 3: rotation 90° anticlockwise, centre (1, 1) then reflection in $y = 1.5$

triangle 4: rotation 90° anticlockwise, centre (3, 5) then reflection in $y = 2$

triangle 5: rotation 90° anticlockwise, centre (–4, 0) then reflection in $y = –6$

triangle 6: rotation 180°, centre (0, 0) then reflection in $x = 1$

Note. There are many other ways of doing each part.

2. (a) rotation 180°, centre (3, 2) then translation $\begin{pmatrix} 1 \\ 0 \end{pmatrix}$ (b) translation $\begin{pmatrix} 3 \\ 0 \end{pmatrix}$ then rotation 180° centre (5, 2)

(c) 90° clockwise, centre (3.5, 0.5) then reflection in $y = 2$

(d) reflection in $x = 3.5$ then rotation 90° clockwise, centre (5, 2)

3. (a) (–2, 4)   (b) (–1, 1)   (c) (1, 1)   (d) (–3, –3)   **4.** (a) (1, 3)   (b) (–8, 4)   (c) (3, 1)

5. (a) (i) rotation 90° clockwise, centre (–1, 5)   (ii) rotation 90° clockwise, centre (–3, 2)

6. (c) (i) rotation 90° clockwise, centre (1, 1)   (ii) rotation 90° clockwise, centre (3, 3)

    (iii) reflection in $y = x – 3$

Page 216   Exercise 1M

1. $3x + 12$ **2.** $5x + 15$ **3.** $4x – 8$ **4.** $6x – 12$ **5.** $4x + 2$ **6.** $6x + 9$ **7.** $12x + 4$ **8.** $12x + 15$

9. $18 – 9x$ **10.** $8x – 10$ **11.** $21x – 7$ **12.** $20x + 50$ **13.** $15x – 25$ **14.** $6 – 4x$ **15.** $3x + 3y$

16. (a) $3(2x + 7)$ (b) $3(4 – 3x)$ (c) $5(2x + 6)$ (d) $4(2a – 7)$ **17.** $5x + 11$ **18.** $5x + 14$

19. $6x + 12$ **20.** $8x + 11$ **21.** $20x + 22$ **22.** $14x + 25$ **23.** $8x – 1$ **24.** $18x + 9$ **25.** $14x + 3$

26. $7x + 6$ **28.** $8x + 14$ **29.** $20x + 15$ **30.** $10x – 7$ **31.** $7x + 9$ **32.** $12x + 9$ **33.** $7x + 14$

34. $27x + 1$ **35.** $19x + 9$ **36.** $19x + 12$ **37.** $7x + 2$ **38.** (a) $7x + 21$ (b) $2x + 20$

Page 217   Exercise 1E

1. $4n + 4$ **2.** $2n + 10$ **3.** $5a + 2$ **4.** $5a + 23$ **5.** $4m + 7$ **6.** $5m + 8$ **7.** $13a + 8b$ **8.** $7a + b$

9. $6a + 6b$ **10.** $3a + 14b$ **11.** $2a + b$ **12.** $5a + 5b$ **13.** (a) $3(n – 2) + 2(n + 1) = 5n – 4$

(b) $5(n + 3) – 3(n + 2) = 2n + 9$ (c) $2(2n – 1) + 3(n + 4) = 7n + 10$ **14.** $2a^2$ **15.** n^2 **16.** $3m^3$

17. $2a^2 + 2a$ **18.** $2n^2 + 6n$ **19.** $a^2 – a$ **20.** n^3 **21.** n^4 **22.** n^2

29. (a)

(b)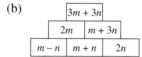

(c)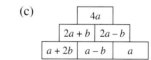

30. (a)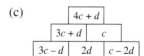

(b)

(c)

(d)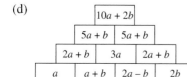

(e)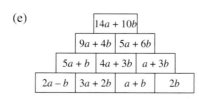

Page 219   **Exercise 2M**

1. 4   **2.** 12   **3.** 14   **4.** 30   **5.** 94   **6.** 20   **7.** 9   **8.** 59   **9.** 3   **10.** 0   **11.** 22   **12.** 9

13. 6   **14.** 30   **15.** 8   **16.** 4   **17.** 3   **18.** $\frac{1}{2}$ **19.** 3   **20.** 4   **21.** 3   **22.** 5   **23.** 11   **24.** 6

25. 2   **26.** 5   **27.** 3   **28.** $\frac{1}{6}$ **29.** 11   **30.** 5   **31.** 6   **32.** 2   **33.** 0   **34.** 5   **35.** 4   **36.** 21

Page 220   **Exercise 2E**

1. 4   **2.** 3   **3.** 3   **4.** 6   **5.** 1   **6.** 4   **7.** 0   **8.** 2   **9.** 1   **10.** $\frac{1}{2}$ **11.** $\frac{1}{4}$ **12.** $\frac{1}{6}$

13. 3   **14.** 7   **15.** 2   **16.** $\frac{1}{6}$ **17.** 2   **18.** 6   **19.** 3   **20.** 0   **21.** 4   **22.** 1   **23.** 7   **24.** $1\frac{1}{2}$

Page 221   **Exercise 3M**

1. 8   **2.** 2.2   **3.** $\frac{3}{5}$ **4.** 75   **5.** $6\frac{1}{2}$ **6.** $2\frac{1}{3}$ **7.** $14\frac{1}{2}$ **8.** 67   **9.** 10   **10.** $\frac{1}{3}$ **11.** 7   **12.** $\frac{1}{2}$ **13.** 3

Page 222   **Exercise 3E**

1. 5   **2.** 2   **3.** 1   **4.** 10   **5.** 5   **6.** 6   **7.** 4   **8.** 3   **9.** 2   **10.** 7   **11.** 2   **12.** 7

13. 4   **14.** 3   **15.** 3   **16.** $\frac{1}{2}$ **17.** 11   **18.** 6   **19.** 8   **20.** 1   **21.** 4   **22.** 2   **23.** 3   **24.** 6

25. 15   **26.** 8   **27.** −1   **28.** 27   **29.** 1   **30.** 0

Page 222   **Exercise 4E**

1. 1   **2.** 2   **3.** 2   **4.** 3   **5.** 1   **6.** 4   **7.** 2   **8.** −1   **9.** −3

10. −4   **11.** 5   **12.** 9   **13.** $\frac{3}{7}$ **14.** $\frac{7}{11}$ **15.** $4\frac{4}{5}$ **16.** $3\frac{7}{8}$ **17.** −3   **18.** 6

Page 223   **Exercise 5M**

1. 6.5   **2.** 12   **3.** 5 cm   **4.** 4 cm   **5.** 5 cm   **6.** (a) 40°   (b) 30°

7. 5   **8.** 20, 21, 22   **9.** 54, 55, 56   **10.** 4   **11.** 5

Page 224   **Exercise 5E**

1. 40   **2.** 40°, 70°, 70°   **3.** $x = 5$, area = 84 cm²   **4.** 7.5 kg   **5.** 2

6. 2.5   **7.** 2.5   **8.** (c) 8   **9.** (a) 11   (b) 9   (c) 19

10. 11 km   **11.** 23, 24, 25, 26   **12.** 51, 53, 55, 57   **13.** 3

14. (a) 3   (b) $2\frac{4}{7}$ **15.** 44   **16.** 10, 12, 14

Page 226   **Exercise 6E**

1. (a)

21	5	26
9		
30		

(b)

7	23	30
4		
11		

(c)

9	15	24
19		
28		

2.

5	12	17
24		
29		

3.

5	3	8
12		
17		

4.

13	9	22
5		
18		

5.

17	15	32
28		
45		

6.

−1	5	4
16		
15		

7.

5	7	12
23		
28		

8.

7	9	16
11		
18		

9.

3	16	19
8		
11		

10.

5	4	9
1	▓	3
6	6	12

11.

11	17	28
18	▓	6
29	5	34

12.

11	8	19
6	▓	2
17	4	21

Page 228 *Check Yourself on Sections 4.6 and 4.7*

1. (a) (i) rotation 90° CW, centre (−1, −1)   (ii) rotation 90° ACW, centre (3, −1)

(iii) reflection in $y = -1$ (iv) reflection in $y = x$ (v) rotation 90° CW, centre (−1, −1)

(b) various e.g. rotation 180°, centre (1, 0) then reflection in $y = 3$ **2.** (a) (i) $4n - 12$ (ii) $7n + 1$

(iii) $n - 2$ (b) (i) 6   (ii) $\dfrac{7}{5}$ (iii) 3   (c) sides 11

Page 229 *Mixed Review*

Part one

1. (a) 072°   (b) 252°   **2.** (a) 8   (b) $\dfrac{11}{7}$ **3.** 7.5 cm   **4.** (a) 0.08   (b) 150

(c) 1000   (d) 0.0006   (e) 3.6   (f) 250   **5.** (a) Not correct: there is no correlation

(b) Teacher's theory is wrong. Those who watched more television did better in the tests.

6. 32   **7.** (a) 91   (b) 49   **8.** (a) 441   (b) 392   **10.** (a) triangle 1   (b) (0, 0)

(c) $x = 1$ (d) triangle 6   **11.** (a) 20, 60   (b) 30, 60

(c) 90 acres on Ash Farm and only 80 acres on Oak Farm.

Part two

1. 13 km   **2.** (c) Maths and Geography: no correlation; History and Geography: strong positive correlation

(d) Pupil I: Maths mark impossible to estimate; History mark about 32.   **4.** (a) (0, 3)   (b) (−2, −2)

5. (a) $2x + 1 = 3x - 6$ (b) $x = 7$, area = 135 cm²   **6.** (b) (i) 4   (ii) 5.8   (iii) 2.2 (all gallons)

(c) 17.5 miles/gallon   **7.** (a) 819   (b) £8840   (c) 639.6 kg   **8.** (a) 74   (b) 18

9. 3   **10.** 54 or 57   **11.** Rotation 90° anticlockwise about (4, 4)

Page 233   **Puzzles and Problems 4**

1. (a) A = 7, B = 12, C= 11, D = 5   (b) P = 8, Q = 5, R = 10, S = 11, T = 2

3.

9	26	33	45
11			
15			
22			

The numbers may be written in any order but 11, 15 and 22 must be on the short side.

4. thirty-one   **5.** $(105 \div 7) \times 3 - 7 = 38$

6. 55 people, £101   **7.**

K	L	G	B	P
D	R	J	C	N

8. E

Page 234   **Finding areas by counting dots**

For $i = 0$, $A = \frac{1}{2}p - 1$

For $i \neq 0$, $A = \frac{1}{2}p + i - 1$. This is Pick's theorem.

Page 236   **Mental Arithmetic Practice**

1. 40	**2.** 0.15	**3.** £16	**4.** True	**5.** 0.22	**6.** 36°
7. ~27 cm²	**8.** £16.60	**9.** Jan	**10.** £50	**11.** 500 cm	**12.** 8 inches
13. 3 h 45 min	**14.** square	**15.** $\frac{2}{5}$	**16.** £5	**17.** 12	**18.** 198
19. 2 hours	**20.** 2700	**21.** 120°	**22.** £8	**23.** £16	**24.** 4
25. 2	**26.** 0.75	**27.** 10,000	**28.** 48 cm²	**29.** 75%	**30.** £330

Page 237   **A long time ago! 4**

1. $6 = 1 + 2 + 3$ **2.** 28   **3.** None

4. (a) eg. 8128 and 8589869056

(c) $2^n - 1$ must be a prime number for the formula to work.

Unit 5

Page 239   *Exercise 1M*

1. ×2   **2, 3, 4.** not enlargements   **5.** ×3   **6.** ×2

Page 239   *Exercise 1E*

8. 120 mm   **9.** 14 cm   **10.** 3.4 cm   **11.** $x = 1$ cm, $y = 18$ cm

Page 243   *Exercise 2E*

9. (f) $\Delta 2$ (1, 6), $\Delta 3$ (5, 6), $\Delta 4$ (8, 3), $\Delta 5$ (10, 11)   **10.** (a) s.f. 6, (13, 6)   (b) s.f. 2, (15, 4)
    (c) s.f. $\frac{2}{3}$, (15, 12)   (d) s.f. 4, (16, 8)   (e) s.f. 3, (15, 6)   **11.** (d) A° (3, 7)
12. (a) s.f. 2, (6, 3)   (b) s.f. 3, (8, 1)   (c) s.f. 4, (9, 1)   (d) s.f. $1\frac{1}{2}$, (14, 1)
    (e) s.f $\frac{3}{4}$, (17, 1)   **14.** (g) Ratios: 4; 9; 16   (h) Ratio of areas = (scale factor)²

Page 247   *Exercise 1M*

1. (a) $12 \to 72$, $n \to 6n$ (b) $8 \to 64$, $n \to 8n$ (c) $15 \to 150$, $n \to 10n$
2. (a) $20 \to 80 \to 81$, $n \to 4n \to 4n + 1$ (b) $12 \to 60 \to 59$, $n \to 5n \to 5n - 1$
3. (a) $3n$ (b) $5n$ (c) n^2 (d) $7n$ (e) $n + 1$ (f) n^3 (g) $2n - 1$
4. (a) $2 - 14 - 15$, $3 - 21 - 22$, $4 - 28 - 29$ (b) $2 - 6 - 4$, $3 - 9 - 7$, $4 - 12 - 10$
    (c) $2 - 10 - 11$, $3 - 15 - 16$, $8 - 40 - 41$ (d) $1 - 10 - 11$, $2 - 20 - 21$, $5 - 50 - 51$, $10 - 100 - 101$

Page 249   *Exercise 1E*

1. (a) 3   (b) 5   (c) 11   **2.** (a) 2   (b) 8   (c) 12   **3.** (a) 3   (b) 5
    (c) 7   (d) 21   **4.** (a) 4   (b) 8   (c) 80   **5.** (a) 6   **6.** 16   (c) 51
6. (a) 18   (b) 15   (c) 9   **7.** (a) 2   (b) 299   **8.** 5, 7, 9, 11, 13
9. (a) 3, 4, 5, 6, 7   (b) 5, 10, 15, 20, 25   (c) 9, 19, 29, 39, 49   (d) −1, 0, 1, 2, 3
    (e) $1, \frac{1}{2}, \frac{1}{3}, \frac{1}{4}, \frac{1}{5}$ (f) 1, 4, 9, 16, 25   **10.** (a) $6n - 3$ (b) $6n$

Page 251   *Exercise 2M*

1. $4n + 1$ **2.** (a) $3n + 4$ (b) $5n - 1$ **3.** $4n + 2$ **4.** $3n + 2$ **5.** (a) $2n + 6$
    (b) $4n - 1$ (c) $5n + 3$ **6.** (a) $8n + 3$ (b) $2n + \frac{1}{2}$ (c) $3n - 10$ **7.** $3n + 1$
8. $3n$ **9.** $4n$

Page 253   *Exercise 2E*

1. $2n + 1$ **2.** $4n + 1$ **3.** $2n + 2$ **4.** $4n + 2$ **5.** $n + 4$
6. $2n + 6$ **7.** $4n + 2$ **8.** $2n + 4$ **9.** $4n + 2$ **11.** $w = 2p + 6$

Page 255   **Vending machine problem**

Amount put in	Number of ways
10p	1
20p	2
30p	3
40p	5
50p	8
60p	13

The numbers are found by adding together the two preceding terms (as in a Fibonacci sequence). So for 70p, there are $(8 + 13)$ ways of putting in the coins. For 120p, there are 233 ways.

Page 256   **Check Yourself Sections 5.1 and 5.2**

2. (a) (i) $4n$ (ii) $2n + 1$ (iii) $n + 2$ (iv) $\dfrac{n}{n + 1}$ (b) (i) 26   (ii) 10001

(c) (i) $3n - 1$ (ii) $7n + 3$ (iii) $4n - 1$

Page 257   **Exercise 1M**

1. (a) $10^2 = 9^2 + 9 + 10$ (b) (i) 961   (ii) 5041   (iii) 10201   (iv) 361

2. 2 orange + 12 cola or 5 orange + 10 cola   **3.** (a) 19824 cm   (b) 0.2 km   **4.** May 1st

5. £1.52   **6.** £118.80   **7.** (a) 7, 11   (b) 11, 35, 67   (c) $-1, -5, -13$ **8.** 255 g

9. 10   **10.** (a) $\dfrac{31}{32}$ (b) $\dfrac{1}{17}$

Page 258   **Exercise 2M**

1. 4 tripods and 6 octopods or 12 tripods and 3 octopods   **2.** [Other ways are possible.]

(a) $16 + 4 + 4$ (b) $49 + 9 + 4$ (c) $400 + 36 + 1 + 1$ (d) $2401 + 25 + 9 + 1$ (e) $6084 + 81 + 25$

(f) $9604 + 289 + 16$ **3.** (a) 1.5 hours   (b) 150 km   **4.** 58 days   **5.** (a) litres

(b) metres   (c) tonnes   (d) hectares   **6.** 17%   **7.** (a) 80000   (b) £34

(c) 499.5   **8.** 144   **9.** 12.2%   **10.** 2, 3, 5

Page 259   **Exercise 3M**

1. (a) $1 + 16 + 64$ **2.** 3375 m   **3.** 11   **4.** 9   **5.** 82p   **6.** 12600

7. 2508   **8.** (a) 6   (b) 9   **9.** 202   **10.** $15 \times 20 \times 30$ (cm)

Page 261   **Exercise 4M**

1. 475   **2.** 31   **3.** (a) 33×38 (b) 34×36 **4.** (a) $12 - 13$ cm   (b) no

5. (b) (i) (4, 3)   (ii) (0, 5)   (c) (i) kite   (ii) parallelogram   (iii) trapezium

(iv) parallelogram   **6.** (a) >   (b) >   (c) <   (d) >   (e) =   (f) >

7. (a) 2 m   (b) 2 litres   (c) 60 g   **8.** £221 089.60   **9.** 63   **10.** (a) $527 - 164$

(b) $538 + 145$ (c) $285 \times 9 = 2565$

Page 262   Exercise 5M

1. £2970   **2.** 11.3 m   **3.** 1500 g bag is better value   **4.** $3799.40   **5.** C   **6.** (a) 145
(b) 4   (c) 50   (d) 450   (e) 713   (f) 5   **7.** 30.6p   **8.** (a) 4900 mm
(b) 1.36 mm/s   (c) 0.0227 mm/s   **9.** 72p   **10.** 199 – 103, 198 – 102, 197 – 101, 196 – 100

Page 265   Exercise 1M

(All in cm)

1. (a) 6.40   (b) 5   (c) 6.32   (d) 13.6   (e) 13   (f) 9.43   (g) 6.71   (h) 9.90
2. (a) 6.93   (b) 6.32   (c) 5.29   (d) 7.94   (e) 4   (f) 4.58   (g) 5   (h) 10.7
3. (a) 8.32   (b) 3.12   (c) 77.6   (d) 29.8   (e) 12.1   (f) 5.66   (g) 2.61   (h) 8.03
4. 4.58 m   **5.** 2.4 m   **6.** 13.6 km   **7.** 45.3 cm   **8.** Rectangle longer by 0.545 cm

Page 267   Exercise 1E

1. (a) $a = 4.90$, $b = 6.71$, $c = 5.66$, $d = 7.14$, $e = 4.69$, $f = 6.42$, $g = 7.55$, $h = 10.8$ **2.** 76.3 km   **3.** 17.0 cm
4. 13.4 feet   **5.** 8.49 cm   **6.** height = 12.1 cm, area = 84.9 cm^2 **7.** 14.1 cm   **8.** 7.4 cm
9. (a) 10 cm   (b) 24 cm^2 (c) 4.8 cm

Page 269   Exercise 2E

1. 282.8 m   **2.** (a) 8.31   (b) 8.06   (c) 3.46   (d) 2.83   (e) 7.21   (f) 5.29
3. 12.5 cm^2 **4.** (a) 5.66   (b) 8.06   (c) 9   **5.** 17.3   **6.** No. Diagonal is 5.59 m.
7. 3 cm   **8.** (a) 4.47   (b) 2   **9.** 106.3 m

Page 270   Check Yourself Section 5.4

1. (a) $\sqrt{41}$ (b) $\sqrt{45}$ (c) $\sqrt{51}$ (d) $\sqrt{504}$ **2.** (a) 31.2 cm^2 (b) 7.35 cm

Page 273   Exercise 1E

6. (c) (3, 5)   **9.** (3, 4)   **10.** (2, 1), (4, 5), (6, 3)   **11.** 12 square units

Page 275   Exercise 2M

1. lines are parallel, $y = x + c$ cuts y-axis at $(0, c)$ **2.** Similar to **1**   **3.** Similar to **1**
4. (a) (0, 7)   (b) (0, –3)   **5.** $y = 6x + c$ **7.** Straight lines are $y = 3x + 2$, $y = 5x – 1$

Page 276   Exercise 2E

1. (6, 9), $y = x + 3$ **2.** (12, 10), $y = x – 2$ **3.** (7, 21), $y = 3x$ **4.** (–1, 1), $y = 2x + 1$
5. (10, 49), $y = 5x – 1$ **6.** (10, –5), $x + y = 5$ **7.** (a) $y = \frac{1}{2}x$, $y = 8$, $y = x + 3$, $x + y = 13$
    (b) $x = 4$, $y = x – 6$ **8.** dots: $y = 3x + 1$; crosses: $y = \frac{1}{2}x$ **9.** dots: $x + y = 8$; crosses: $y = x – 2$
10. (a) $x = 3$ (b) $x + y = 16$ (c) $y = 2x$ (d) $y = x$ (e) $y = \frac{1}{3}x$ (f) $3y + x = 24$

Page 278   ***Exercise 3E***

7. (a) Lowest value of y is -2.25. It occurs when $x = 1\frac{1}{2}$.   **8.** $y = 8$ **9.** $x = 1.9, 2.4$

Page 279   ***Exercise 4M***

1. (a) £26   (b) £60   (c) 400 miles   **2.** (a) (i) 79%   (ii) 30%   (b) 48 marks
3. (a) (i) £2.50   (ii) €3.40   (b) (i) £4   (ii) £3   (c) (i) £24000   (ii) £20000
   (d) More expensive   **4.** (b) (i) 68°F   (ii) 14°F   (iii) 10°C   (c) Stay at home
5. (a) 2.5 km per litre   (b) 14 m.p.g.   (c) 4 gallons   **6.** (a) £50   (b) £15
   (e) Maggie cheaper for more than 40 pages

Page 281   ***Exercise 1M***

1. 4:1   **2.** 7:6   **3.** 2:3   **4.** 2:1   **5.** (a) 3:2   (b) 3:2   (c) 3:1
6. (a) 3:2   (b) 3:5   (c) 1:4   (d) 12:11   (e) 3:4   (f) 8:5   **7.** 15
8. 21   **9.** 500   **10.** 41:14   **11.** (a) 3:2:4   (b) 8:1:3   (c) 6:5:4   (d) 3:2:3
   (e) 7:1:5   (f) 2:1:5   **12.** 8 peaches, 16 bananas   **13.** 30 home wins, 5 draws
14. 28 sheep, 21 cows   **15.** (a) 1:2   (b) 1:3   (c) 1:3   **16.** 2:3   **17.** $\frac{3}{7}$

Page 283   ***Exercise 1E***

1. Saffon 18, Sam 12   **2.** mother £45, son £15   **3.** (a) 24 cm, 30 cm   (b) £36, £63
   (c) 72 km, 60 km   (d) £8, £12, £16   (e) 100 kg, 40 kg, 60 kg   (f) £200, £1800   **4.** 330 g
5. 6 tonnes   **6.** 6 black, 14 white   **7.** (a) 5:7   (b) 25:49   **8.** 45 g   **9.** 1:5   **10.** 2:5
11. 1:5   **12.** 1:10   **13.** 5:6:30   **14.** 3:7:30   **15.** 1:168   **16.** 90°, 30°, 60°
17. 120°   **18.** 12 cm, 4 cm

Page 284   ***Exercise 2E***

1. (a) $3\frac{1}{3}$ (b) $2\frac{1}{4}$ **2.** 1.5 litres   **3.** 2.6 cm   **4.** (a) 6   (b) 10   **5.** 5:4
6. £200 000   **7.** (a) 1:2   (b) 3 litres   (c) 4 litres   **8.** 45p   **9.** 28 years
10. 5:6   **11.** 2:5   **12.** 5:3
13. (a) The ratio approaches a value of about 1.618. This ratio is called the golden section. It is a ratio which
      is pleasing to the eye and occurs in Greek architecture. Ordinary postcards have their sides in the ratio
      of about 1.618

Page 286   ***Exercise 3M***

1. 30 m   **2.** 8 m   **3.** 400 m   **4.** 7 km   **5.** 90 km   **6.** 1:2500
7. 500 m   **8.** 1 km   **9.** 120 km

Page 287   ***Exercise 3E***

1. 60 cm   **2.** 15 cm   **3.** 17 km   **5.** 162 km   **6.** 1.35 cm
7. 1:190 080   **8.** 1:150 000   **9.** 12 hectares (120 000 m²)   **10.** 1000 cm²

Page 288   **Exercise 1M**

1. A, D, H, K, M not congruent to any other shape. Congruent pairs are B/F, C/L, E/J, G/I

4. (a) 6   (b) scalene 6, equilateral 1   **5.** (a) BC   (b) BD   (c) DBC   (d) ACF

Page 291   **Check Yourself Sections 5.5 and 5.6**

1. (b) $y = 2x + 3$ **2.** 0.25   **3.** (a) 1.75 pints   (b) 0.85 litres   (c) 2.1 pints

4. (a) (i) 2:4:5   (ii) 2:5:7   (b) £80, £140   (c) 4.5   (d) 400   (e) 2 km

Page 292   **Mixed Review**

Part one

1. 2:3   **2.** (b) $(\frac{1}{3}, 0)$ **3.** (1.7, 0), (–1.7, 0)   **4.** (a) 8.74 cm   (b) 4.74 cm   (c) 2.24 cm

6. (a) (i) 0.22   (ii) 0.625   (iii) 0.07   (b) 65%   (c) 0.01, 10%, 0.11, $\frac{1}{9}$

7. (a) Rotation, 90° anticlockwise about (2, 5)   (b) Reflection in $x = -1$ (c) Reflection in $y = x$

   (d) Enlargement, scale factor 3, centre (5, 3)   **8.** 88.55 litres   **9.** (a) 18   (b) 25

10. (b, w): (3, 3), (5, 10) (7, 21)   (c) 55   (d) 17

Part two

1. (a) 80 km/h   (b) 40 km/h   (c) 10 km   (d) 43.6 km/h   **2.** 4 cm   **3.** 36°, 54°, 90°

4. (a) 1.2   (b) 8 (or – 8)   **5.** (a) 7:19   (b) 1750   **6.** (b) (i) Rotation 180°, centre (3, 1)

   (ii) Enlargement, scale factor 3, centre (4, 5)   **7.** 10%   **8.** (a) 6.93 cm   (b) 27.7 cm²

9. (a) $y = x + 3$ (b) $y = 2x + 3$ **10.** (a) 28.3 cm   (b) 34.6 cm

11. (a) Route 1, on main roads, is quicker   (b) 0.107 hours   **12.** (a) 1:5   (b) 1:1   **13.** 90 m

Page 297 **Puzzles and Problems 5**

Crossnumbers

1.

2	3	5		2	3
5	3	9		5	7
8	7		2	4	5
1		2	7	0	8
4	2		1	4	6
	6	9	5		

2.

4	2	1	5		2	4	7
6	4		4	2	1	3	
5	4	3	7	4		1	8
1		6	0	8		7	7
4	3	9	4		4		2
	3	1		2	1	6	3
4	2	8	3		3	3	4
7			3	3	3		

3.

1		6	6	1	5	2	
4	2	3	5	8	2	4	
5	2			5	4	5	2
	8	9	6		8		4
6	6	1	4	5		5	6
2		6	6	2	7	2	
4	3	7		3	7	4	
1	6	1	4	5		9	0

4.

1	4	7	8		2	9	1	6	3
4	3		2	5	2	3		1	4
2	9	6	1	3		5	6	0	1
5		3	4	1		4	7	9	8
1	9	7	6		1	2	3		2
	8	1		8	4	3	5	9	
1	3	2	5		5	4	8	7	5
6	5		6	7	0			2	6
8	1	7	1		2	9	8	7	2
7	4	0	1	3	6		2	3	1

5.

3	5	1	4		2	9	6	6	6
1	9		3	5	1	7		9	0
8	2	6	1	4		3	4	3	7
7		2	0	6		3	0	4	8
3	2	1	4		2	7	6		3
	3	1		9	3	6	5	4	
3	5	4	4		5	4	7	3	2
2	8		1	3	7			1	5
4	1	2	2		8	0	7	5	1
4	5	2	7	0	5		7	8	3

Page 299 **Diagonals**

(a) 13   (b) (i) 20   (ii) 29   (c) 289   (d) 400   (e) 60

Page 299 **A long time ago! 5**

1. 7   **2.** 15   **3.** 3   **4.** 31   **5.** 127

6. About 585 000 000 000 years

Page 301 **Mental Arithmetic Practice**

1. 1	**2.** 1.25	**3.** ten million	**4.** 80 cm²	**5.** 80%	**6.** £1040
7. 30 m	**8.** 102	**9.** 4%	**10.** 60p	**11.** 30	**12.** 10 km
13. 566	**14.** 2nd of July	**15.** 53	**16.** 5%	**17.** 45 kg	**18.** 24 cm²
19. 300	**20.** 96 cm	**21.** £1.44	**22.** ~ 30	**23.** £16	**24.** 25 miles
25. £3.87	**26.** 210°	**27.** 36	**28.** 18°	**29.** 2 h 25 min	**30.** hexagon

Unit 6

Page 302   *Exercise 1M*

1. 5   **2.** 6   **3.** $\frac{1}{7}$ **4.** $\frac{1}{2}$ **5.** 5   **6.** $\frac{1}{2}$ **7.** 2   **8.** 4

9. $\frac{2}{3}$ **10.** $-\frac{1}{6}$ **11.** -1 **12.** -7 **13.** -4 **14.** $2\frac{3}{5}$ **15.** 1   **16.** $\frac{1}{9}$

17. $\frac{3}{10}$ **18.** 4   **19.** $-2\frac{2}{9}$ **20.** -13 **21.** $\frac{1}{3}$ **22.** -3 **23.** $-\frac{1}{2}$ **24.** 0

Page 303   *Exercise 1E*

1. 12   **2.** 10   **3.** 20   **4.** -14 **5.** -25 **6.** $1\frac{1}{2}$ **7.** $2\frac{2}{3}$ **8.** $\frac{4}{5}$

9. $\frac{6}{7}$ **10.** $\frac{4}{9}$ **11.** 2   **12.** 12   **13.** $2\frac{2}{3}$ **14.** 15   **15.** $-\frac{8}{11}$ **16.** -50

17. 12   **18.** 18   **19.** -5 **20.** 12   **21.** 22   **22.** 51   **23.** 3   **24.** $1\frac{1}{4}$

25. 6   **26.** 24   **27.** 4   **28.** 6   **29.** $\frac{1}{2}$ **30.** -4 **31.** $2\frac{1}{2}$ **32.** $\frac{1}{2}$

Page 304   *Exercise 2M*

1. -2 **2.** $3\frac{1}{3}$ **3.** $5\frac{1}{2}$ **4.** $-1\frac{2}{5}$ **5.** $-1\frac{2}{21}$ **6.** $\frac{1}{2}$

7. 4   **8.** $1\frac{2}{3}$ **9.** $2\frac{1}{9}$ **10.** $1\frac{3}{4}$ **11.** $1\frac{2}{3}$ **12.** -6

13. $-\frac{1}{3}$ **14.** $-\frac{1}{3}$ **15.** 0   **16.** $3\frac{1}{3}$ **17.** $\frac{1}{2}$ **18.** 0

Page 305   *Exercise 2E*

1. $4\frac{1}{5}$ **2.** $5\frac{1}{2}$ **3.** -1 **4.** $\frac{5}{6}$ **5.** -6 **6.** $2\frac{4}{5}$

7. $\frac{5}{18}$ **8.** $\frac{3}{4}$ **9.** $2\frac{2}{11}$ **10.** $\frac{1}{3}$ **11.** $\frac{1}{8}$ **12.** 7

Page 306   *Exercise 3M*

1. (a) $2\frac{1}{2}$ (b) $3\frac{1}{5}$ **2.** 5   **3.** $x = 54°$. Angles are $54°, 63°, 63°$ **4.** 7 cm

5. £11   **6.** £11   **7.** 9 km   **8.** 61, 62, 63, 64   **9.** 33, 35, 37, 39   **10.** 28

Page 307   *Exercise 3E*

1. 5   **2.** 9   **3.** 11   **4.** 17   **5.** 28   **6.** 280 cm²   **7.** (a) 2   (b) 3

   (c) 5   (d) 6   **8.** 4 m × 12 m   **9.** $35°, 40°, 105°$ **10.** 18   **11.** (a) 3   (b) 7

Page 311   *Exercise 1M*

1. 30 cm³   **2.** 32 cm³   **3.** 72 cm³   **4.** 48 cm³   **5.** 54 cm³   **6.** 15 mm³   **7.** 20 cm³

8. 22 cm³   **9.** 28 cm³   **10.** (a) 32 m³   (b) 64 m²   **11.** (a) 115 cm³   (b) 210 cm³   **12.** 512

Page 312   *Exercise 1E*

1. 125 cm³   **2.** 4200 m³   **3.** 2 hours   **4.** 5.88 m   **5.** (a) 8 cm³   (b) 8 cm³

   (c) 6 cm³   **6.** 300 000 cm³   **7.** 6 hours 40 minutes   **8.** (a) $x = 2.5$ cm   (b) $x = 3$ cm

(c) $x = 1.5$ cm   (d) $x = 1$ cm   (e) $x = 1.5$ cm   (f) $x = 5$ cm   **10.** 84   **11.** (a) abc cm^3

(b) $2(ab + ac + bc)$ cm^2 **12.** 50 cm

Page 315   **Exercise 2M**

1. 24 cm^3 **2.** 77 m^3 **3.** 150 cm^3 **4.** 40 cm^3 **5.** 21 m^3 **6.** 115 cm^3

7. 210 cm^3 **8.** 160 cm^3 **9.** 584 cm^3

Page 316   **Exercise 2E**

1. 7.5 cm^2 **2.** 12 m   **3.** 80 litres   **4.** 120 litres   **5.** 1648 cm^3 **6.** 1 hour 40 minutes

7. 5 cm   **8.** 13   **9.** 14.8 kg   **10.** 8 h 45 mins

Page 318   **Exercise 3M**

1. (a) 302 cm^3 (b) 137 cm^3 (c) 29.0 cm^3 (d) 763 cm^3 (e) 157 cm^3 (f) 385 cm^3

2. (a) 251 cm^3 (b) 63.6 cm^3 **3.** 176 litres   **4.** 14.4 cm^3 **5.** 0.503 cm^3 **6.** 2510 m^3

7. No. There is 167 cm^3 left over   **8.** 61 min   **9.** 558.5 cm^3

Page 319   **Exercise 3E**

1. 10.0 cm   **2.** 14   **3.** 3270 cm^3 **4.** 63.7 cm   **5.** 259 times

6. (a) Whole box, volume = 110 cm^3. One portion, volume = 12.2 cm^3 (b) 13.8 grams

7. 11 100 cm^3 (i.e. $\pi \times 14^2 \times 18$)   **8.** 1.43 cm   **9.** 6.44 cm

Page 321   **Check Yourself Sections 6.1 and 6.2**

1. (a) (i) $\frac{1}{3}$ (ii) 1   (iii) 1.5   (b) (i) $1\frac{1}{3}$ (ii) 18   (c) 150 cm^2

2. (a) (i) 33 cm^3 (ii) 905 cm^3 (b) 55 cm

Page 322   **Exercise 1M**

Pythagoras knew his squares

Page 323   **Exercise 2M**

1. (a) £29.15   (b) £85.75   (c) £0.31   (d) £1.35   **2.** (a) 0.62   (b) 0.06

(c) 0.08   (d) 0.032   (e) 0.175   (f) 1.25   **3.** 65%   **4.** 4%

5. (a) 38.9%   (b) 8.3%   **6.** 8.2%   **7.** (a) 62.5%   (b) 6.6%   **8.** (a) 10.4%

(b) 40.2%   **9.** (a) 53.9%   (b) 50.5%   (c) 58.7%   **10.** 59   **11.** (a) 2%

(b) $\frac{45}{120}$

Page 325   **Exercise 2E**

1. (a) 1.08   (b) 1.1   (c) 0.97   (d) 0.85   **2.** £9009   **3.** £79.05

4. (a) £14.89   (b) £2816   (c) £237.49   (d) £6 174 000   **5.** £9 370 000   **6.** 1.5

7. 106.48 cm^3 **8.** A 46 squares, B 38 squares, C 26 squares   **9.** 513 g   **10.** £105 792

11. (a) 583   (b) 1210   **12.** (a) £48.38   (b) £933.93

Page 327 **Exercise 1M**

1. (a) $\frac{1}{4}$ (b) $\frac{3}{4}$ (c) $\frac{1}{52}$ (d) $\frac{51}{52}$ **2.** (a) $\frac{1}{7}$ (b) $\frac{6}{7}$ (c) $\frac{5}{7}$

(d) $\frac{2}{7}$ **3.** (a) $\frac{1}{8}$ (b) $\frac{7}{8}$ (c) $\frac{3}{8}$ (d) $\frac{1}{4}$ **4.** 0.39 **5.** (a) $\frac{1}{965}$

(b) $\frac{964}{965}$ **6.** (a) $\frac{1}{6}$ (b) $\frac{1}{3}$ **7.** (a) $\frac{1}{8}$ (b) $\frac{1}{8}$ (c) $\frac{1}{2}$ (d) $\frac{5}{8}$

8. $\frac{2}{3}$ **9.** (a) $\frac{2}{9}$ (b) $\frac{2}{3}$ **10.** Syline **11.** (a) $\frac{5}{16}$ (b) $\frac{15}{16}$ (c) $\frac{1}{16}$

Page 330 **Exercise 1E**

1. (a) 80 (b) 240 **2.** (a) 300 (b) 150 (c) 100 (d) 100

3. (a) 116 (b) 420 **4.** (a) 50 (b) 150 **5.** (a) $\frac{1}{7}$ (b) 5 balls numbered '4'

6. (a) $\frac{5}{9}$ (b) $\frac{4}{9}$ (c) $\frac{1}{9}$ (d) $\frac{6}{11}$ **7.** (a) $\frac{1}{5}$ (b) $\frac{1}{21}$

(c) 0 **8.** (a) $\frac{3}{49}$ (b) $\frac{12}{49}$ **9.** 91% **10.** (a) $\frac{2}{5}$ (b) could be 3 red, 2 black

(c) various answers **11.** $\frac{1}{7}$ **12.** $\frac{n}{m+n}$ **13.** (a) £27 (b) 90

(c) 90 (d) £4.50 **14.** £10 **15.** (a) $360\,x$ (b) $200(1-x)$

Page 333 **Exercise 2M**

2. (a) $\frac{1}{9}$ (b)

Total	2	3	4	5	6	7	8	9	10	11	12
Probability	$\frac{1}{36}$	$\frac{2}{36}$	$\frac{3}{36}$	$\frac{4}{36}$	$\frac{5}{36}$	$\frac{6}{36}$	$\frac{5}{36}$	$\frac{4}{36}$	$\frac{3}{36}$	$\frac{2}{36}$	$\frac{1}{36}$

3. (a) $\frac{1}{6}$ (b) $\frac{5}{36}$ **4.** (a) $\frac{1}{6}$ (b) $\frac{1}{6}$ **5.** (a) 8 outcomes (b) (i) $\frac{3}{8}$ (ii) $\frac{1}{8}$

6. (a) 16 outcomes (b) (i) $\frac{3}{8}$ (ii) $\frac{1}{4}$ (iii) $\frac{1}{16}$ **7.** (a) 32 (b) $\frac{1}{32}$

Page 334 **Exercise 2E**

1. (a) (1p, 10p), (1p, 20p), (10p, 20p) (b) (i) $\frac{1}{3}$ (ii) $\frac{1}{3}$ **2.** (a) (2, 3), (2, 6), (2, 7), (3, 6), (3, 7), (6, 7)

(b) (i) $\frac{1}{6}$ (ii) $\frac{1}{3}$ **3.** (a) $\frac{1}{6}$ (b) $\frac{1}{3}$ (c) $\frac{1}{6}$ **4.** (a) $\frac{1}{12}$

(b) $\frac{1}{4}$ **5.** (i) $\frac{1}{7}$ (ii) $\frac{3}{14}$ **6.** (b) (i) $\frac{3}{25}$ (iii) $\frac{1}{50}$ (c) 1

Page 336 **Exercise 3M**

1. (a) $\frac{1}{6}$ (b) $\frac{31}{60}$ **2.** (a) $\frac{1}{2}$ (b) $\frac{61}{150}$ (c) Jenny, more trials

3. (a) $\frac{18}{40}$ (b) $\frac{10}{40}$ (c) $\frac{41}{80}$ (d) $\frac{18}{80}$ Yes: more results

Page 337 **Check Yourself Sections 6.3 and 6.4**

Part 1

1. (a) (i) £34.08 (ii) £89.10 (b) (i) 144 cm^2 (ii) 158.76 cm^2 (c) 17%

Part 2

1. (a) (i) $\frac{1}{4}$ (ii) $\frac{1}{6}$ (b) (i) $\frac{1}{4}$ (ii) $\frac{5}{12}$ **2.** (b) (i) $\frac{1}{18}$ (ii) $\frac{5}{9}$

Page 339   ***Exercise 1M***

1. (a) 2   (b) 4   (c) 5   **2.** Eight shapes can be made.

4. A: 3, 8, 9   B: 1, 7   C: 2, 6, 12   D: 4, 5, 10   11 is odd one out

6. (a)   (b)   (c)

Page 346   ***Mixed Review Unit 6***
Part one

1. (a) $\frac{1}{52}$ (b) $\frac{1}{13}$ (c) $\frac{1}{4}$ **2.** (a) $\frac{1}{5}$ (b) $\frac{3}{10}$ (c) $\frac{1}{2}$

3. 1000   **4.** (a) (i) 1 m³   (ii) 1 000 000 cm³   (b) 1 000 000; 2 400 000; 1000 000 000

5. (a) 6   (b) 25   (c) 4   (d) 27   (e) −2   (f) 4

     (g) 3   (h) 39   **6.** (a) top number is $3x + 25$ (b) 7   **8.** 1607

9. $\frac{5}{6}$ **10.** (a) 1160 cm³   (b) 9420 cm³   (c) 2260 cm³   **11.** 196   **12.** £12500

Part two

1. (a) 0.8   (b) 27   (c) $2\frac{2}{7}$ (d) 36

2. $\frac{1}{2}$ **3.** 3   **4.** 9.42 cm   **5.** 1656 g   **6.** 50°, 65°, 65°

7. (a) 16.25%   (b) 4202.5 kg   **8.** (a) 30 cm³   (b) 39.93 cm³   (c) 33.1%

9. (a) 0.576 m³   (b) 0.157 m³   **10.** 20 cm   **11.** (b) (i) $\frac{1}{12}$ (ii) $\frac{1}{6}$

     (iii) $\frac{1}{6}$ **12.** (a) (i) $\frac{1}{9}$ (ii) $\frac{5}{18}$ (b) 1   **13.** (a) $2c - 2$

     (b) $m^2 + 2m$ (c) $3xy$ (d) m^6 (e) $2c^2$ (f) $x^2 + 2x$

     (g) a^3 (h) $\frac{2}{t}$ (i) 2